PENGUIN BOOKS

AROUND THE HEARTH

Dr Kynpham Sing Nongkynrih, poet, writer, and translator, was born on 4 April 1964 in Cherrapunjee, Meghalaya. He belongs to the Khasi tribe and writes in both Khasi and English. His short stories have been published in leading journals in India and translated into Hindi and Bengali. Nongkynrih works as Reader in the Department of English, North-Eastern Hill University (NEHU), Shillong. He edits the university newsletter, *NEHU News*, and the first poetry journal in Khasi, *Rilum*, besides being the associate editor of the university's official journal, *The NEHU Journal*. He was awarded a 'Fellowship for Outstanding Artists 2000' by the Government of India. He also received the first North-East Poetry Award in 2004 from the North-East India Poetry Council, Tripura.

He has a total of five publications in Khasi and three in English besides edited volumes and translation works of poetry and short stories in both Khasi and English.

Around the Hearth
Khasi Legends

KYNPHAM SING NONGKYNRIH

Illustrations by Pankaj Thapa

PENGUIN BOOKS

PENGUIN BOOKS
Published by the Penguin Group
Penguin Books India Pvt. Ltd, 11 Community Centre, Panchsheel Park,
New Delhi 110 017, India
Penguin Group (USA) Inc., 375 Hudson Street, New York, New York 10014, USA
Penguin Group (Canada), 90 Eglinton Avenue East, Suite 700, Toronto,
Ontario, M4P 2Y3, Canada (a division of Pearson Penguin Canada Inc.)
Penguin Books Ltd, 80 Strand, London WC2R 0RL, England
Penguin Ireland, 25 St Stephen's Green, Dublin 2, Ireland
(a division of Penguin Books Ltd)
Penguin Group (Australia), 250 Camberwell Road, Camberwell,
Victoria 3124, Australia (a division of Pearson Australia Group Pty Ltd)
Penguin Group (NZ), 67 Apollo Drive, Rosedale, North Shore 0632,
New Zealand (a division of Pearson New Zealand Ltd)
Penguin Group (South Africa) (Pty) Ltd, 24 Sturdee Avenue, Rosebank,
Johannesburg 2196, South Africa

Penguin Books Ltd, Registered Offices: 80 Strand, London WC2R 0RL, England

First published by Penguin Books India 2007

Copyright © Kynpham Sing Nongkynrih 2007

10 9 8 7 6 5 4 3 2 1

ISBN 10: 0143103016   ISBN 13: 9780143103011

Typeset in *Goudy Old Style* by SÜRYA, New Delhi
Printed at Repro India Ltd., Navi Mumbai

Contents

Prelude

The Khasis, by which I mean all the seven sub-tribes—Khynriam, Pnar, Bhoi, War, Maram, Lyngngam and the now never-heard-of Diko—of the Khasi tribe of North-East India, are a great storytelling people: 'telling', because their alphabet is of very recent history, no older than when Thomas Jones, the Welsh Presbyterian missionary, introduced the Roman script in 1842, to form the essentials of the Khasi written word.

But the alphabet is nothing to judge the Khasi people by. Enlightenment did not come to them with schools and colleges. The Khasis, before the white man came, were not a band of barbarians roving the hills for heads and scalps. They did not live up trees like monkeys, nor hunt for food like savages. They knew how to till the earth and sow their crops. They knew how to make things out of wood and iron; they knew trade and commerce—and yes, industry.

Theirs was a society of great wisdom and civilized conduct at a time when brute force held sway. True enough, they had their fair share of wars and bloodshed, but more importantly, they wanted peace and togetherness with other people, for theirs was a culture that worshipped God through respect for both man and Nature, and indeed all animals and animated things, as creations of God that were equal to each other.

That is why the Khasi stories always begin with 'When man and beasts and stones and trees spoke as one....' This shows the Khasi world view, that sees the universe as a cosmic whole that receives its animation and force from the one living truth, their God, U Blei.

The great storytelling tradition of the Khasis goes back to the time of their creation myths. One of these myths tells us about how one of our ancestors had lost a manuscript, made of a very delicate material and containing our philosophical and religious teachings, as well as the script used to record these teachings. The man was returning from a communion with God at the summit of a very tall mountain. Here, he was familiarized with the history of his race and initiated into certain religious rites and moral principles which were to govern the spiritual, moral and even daily activities of his community. With him was a representative of the people from the plains of Surma. Both were carrying with them precious manuscripts bestowed by God Himself, to make the propagation of His teachings easier. But as they were approaching home, they encountered an overwhelming hurdle in the form of a wide, raging river. The man from Surma, used to swimming in turbulent water, attached his document to a tuft of hair on his pate and contrived to swim across safely.

The Khasi, not wanting to be left behind, took his document between his teeth and, against his better judgement, attempted to cross the river too. But being a hillman, not accustomed to swimming in surging torrents, he soon found himself floundering midstream, with his head bobbing in and out of the water. In trying to save himself and gulping air through his mouth, he accidentally swallowed his document, which by then had been reduced to a pulpy mass. And although, after a huge struggle, he managed to save himself, he had to return to his people empty-handed.

On reaching home, the errant ambassador recounted everything that had happened to a very disappointed people. But he quickly appeased them by assuring them that all God had revealed to him was still fresh in his mind, and that he could easily pass on the teachings to the people by word of mouth. Therefore, a council of all members of the Khasi tribe was convened, wherein the man instructed each person on the teachings of God and His divine laws.

It was from that time that the tradition of storytelling among the Khasis was supposed to have started. The stories began with an exposition showing how the world was created and how Man had come down from heaven to inhabit the earth and populate its wilderness. From here they progressed to the Khasi world view, their concept of God and religion, their concept of good and evil, their matrilineal social structure, their clan system, their democratic governance— and so forth. These constitute the creation myths, or what the Khasis call *khanatang*, or sanctified stories,

The function of such stories is to elucidate the Khasi philosophical thought on every aspect of Khasi culture and make sure that it reaches and holds captive even the simplest of men. The stories are therefore invested with symbolical significance and deliberately rendered interesting so as to beguile listeners into believing that they are hearing a story and not listening to a sermon. For example, when the Khasis speak of *Ka Jingkieng Ksiar* (the Golden Ladder) located at *Lum Sohpet Bneng* (the Mount of Heaven's Navel) and how the Khasi people, in a Golden Age of their existence, used to travel between heaven and earth through the Golden Ladder, they only mean to impress on the listener that the Golden Ladder is actually a golden heart, a virtuous soul, which stands as the only link between Man and God. And when they speak of the Mount of Heaven's Navel, they only wish to illustrate their belief that the relationship between Man and God is like the sacred relationship between mother and child, with the navel and the umbilical cord as the central symbols. It is very important, therefore, to understand the allegorical nature of the stories, so that they are not simply read as fantastic tales from yet another exotic tribal culture.

Thus far, I have been talking only about the khanatang and their function. But the intentions of the Khasi folk stories cannot be confined to philosophical and religious enlightenment alone. Having realized the tremendous potential of the khanatang, the Khasis invented a story for everything. The phenomenon of lightning and thunder; a gigantic boulder that looks like an overturned conical basket; the name of a waterfall; a hill; a forest; a village...everything. To explain the inexplicable, to comprehend the incomprehensible, they always found a story. A moral lesson? They invented another. Young Khasis were instructed in this way by elders, and their school was always the hearth around which they gathered after a day's labour, entertained by both fire and tales. Entertainment was, in fact, the overt purpose, the overriding factor and the informing soul of such stories. And the Khasis may be said to have taught with delight.

In order to serve this twin objective of instruction and entertainment, the old Khasis had to invent many, many stories indeed. In fact, there are thousands of stories floating in each Khasi *hima* (a democratic state governed by a *dorbar hima* or council of state, which is led by a *syiem* or king, who is only a titular head), *raid* (province) and village. These stories were handed down orally, through successive generations, from village raconteurs to the community; from uncles to nephews; and from parents and grandparents to children. And they include among them *khana pateng* (legends), *purinam* (fairy tales), *puriskam* (fables), *khana pharshi* (parables) and, sometimes, true stories that have worked their way into the hearts of one and all. All these may be found in this volume, which may be treated, however, merely as a prelude to other, much more substantial collections in times to come.

Kynpham Sing Nongkynrih

Shillong,
6 June 2006

The Seven Clans

*I*n the beginning there was nothing but a vast emptiness on Earth. God had created only two beings—Ramew, the guardian spirit of Earth, and her husband Basa, who later came to be identified with the patron god of villages. The two lived happily enough for a time, but one thing began to plague their minds: they had no children. They wanted children, wanted them intensely, because Ramew and Basa realized life without them would be terribly lonely and monotonous. They prayed to their God, U Blei, to bless them with at least a child—or two—so that their line could continue.

'O God, our Master, our Creator! O God, Giver and Keeper of Life!' they called upon him. 'We have been living on

Earth, absolutely alone, for many years now. While we love each other and are happy with our own company, we wish our love to be fruitful. We wish to have children, the product of our love, children who would lighten our days and ease the monotony of our existence. It doesn't seem right, O God, Keeper and Giver of Life, that the Earth you created should remain barren and empty like this. O Master Creator! We have each other now, but what about the future?'

After many such entreaties, God granted them their wish and gave them five children of great powers and accomplishments, five children that people have come to call elemental forces. The Sun was their first daughter, followed by their only son, the Moon, and three other daughters, Water, Wind and Fire. Fire was the last born, the womb-cleaning one, and it was always her duty to be at home, to cook their meals and tend to their daily needs as custom demanded.

Ramew was delighted to see her children grow up and prosper. She was particularly delighted to see how they worked at reshaping the world into a pleasant land, giving life to tall trees and beautiful flowers everywhere.

And yet, amidst all that plenty and peace, there seemed to be something wanting. That such loveliness should go untended and uncared for! That such plenty should benefit no one! It was not right, she felt. Ramew turned to God again.

'O God, our Master, our Creator! O God, Giver and Keeper of Life!' she beseeched Him. 'Please forgive me if I seem ungrateful and unhappy with my lot. I am indeed contented and pleased to see my children so powerful and accomplished. They have done wonders here on Earth. They have turned it into a pleasant land of peace and plenty. There are trees and beautiful flowers everywhere. There are fruits and plants of every kind and description. But it pains me to see that so much loveliness and abundance may one day go to waste, with no one to benefit from them. Because, my God, my Creator, my children, though bestowed with outstanding gifts, powers and accomplishments, are yet ill-equipped to look after all that they have created. The Sun and the Moon are too busy roaming the universe, tending to their myriad duties. Water has its limitations and cannot travel the world freely. Wind is not suited for caretaking on her own, nor is Fire. Both of them can run wild if not properly tended. You see, my Lord, we need someone who would not only be the heir to all this bounty but someone who would be a caretaker of all these creations and watch over all my children, so that they do not become excessively wayward.'

God, who understood the yearning of Ramew and who had watched her labour hard and long to make the world a fitting place for life, promised to indulge her wishes. He issued a decree declaring two powerful spirits of the mountains as the guardians of Earth.

But instead of seeing to the welfare of the many living things, these sibling spirits began to tussle for power. This resulted in a terrible fratricidal battle, the scars of which can be seen till today.[1]

Responding to the complaints of Ramew against the mountain spirits, God then placed the responsibility of ruling Earth on animals, with the Tiger as the presiding administrator. But this also did not work as the Tiger began to rule like a despotic overlord and encouraged the law of 'might is right' everywhere.

When, eventually, matters went out of control and degenerated into a state of pandemonium, Ramew once more raised her complaints with God and pleaded with Him for wise and conscientious overseers who would be a blessing on and not a curse to life on Earth.

God, who is just and benevolent, listened with sympathy to the pleas of Ramew and came to the conclusion that none but the sixteen clans living in Heaven would be fitting caretakers of Earth. Accordingly, he summoned the greatest council ever held in Heaven to elect the future guardians of Earth. After days of careful deliberation, God eventually declared that seven of the sixteen clans living in Heaven should descend to Earth, to till the land, to populate the wilderness, to rule and govern and be the crown of all creation. And from then on they would be known as the 'Hynñiew Trep', or the Seven Huts, the Seven Families, the Seven Clans, who would later become the ancestors of the seven sub-tribes of the Khasi people, encompassing the Khynriam, Pnar, Bhoi, War, Maram, Lyngngam and the now never-heard-of Diko.

God who had provided for happiness on Earth, endowing its soil with riches and the fruits of plenty through the children of Ramew, then made a covenant with the Seven Clans and as a token of that covenant, He planted a divine tree on a sacred mount called Lum Sohpet Bneng, which served as the Golden Ladder between the kingdom of God and the kingdom of Man. This covenant declared that so long as the Seven Clans adhered to the three principles of *Ka Tip Briew Tip Blei*, *Ka Tip Kur Tip Kha* and *Ka Kamai ia ka Hok*, that is, so long as they were secure in the Knowledge of Man and God, in the Knowledge of one's Maternal and Paternal Relations, and so long as they lived on Earth in such a way as to earn Righteousness, they would never be left alone, but could come and go as they pleased between Heaven and Earth, through the Golden Ladder at Lum Sohpet Bneng—literally, the Mount of Heaven's Navel. The mountain is so called because it acted as an umbilical cord between God and Man, for even as a child is joined with the mother through this thread of flesh and blood, so also is Man joined with God.

Everything was now well with the world. And as long as Man remembered God and his divine decree, as long as he behaved in a manner befitting his celestial lineage, he prospered in life and never suffered real grief in any way. His life on Earth was one long tale of happiness.

But it is not in Man to be content with happiness alone. Like everything else in this world, he is essentially two-edged, capable at once of great good and great evil. Soon, he began to tire of tirelessly following the dictates of God; he wanted to branch out on his own, to determine his life independently, according to his own instincts and inclinations. In this manner he strayed away from the principles of Ka Tip Briew Tip Blei, Ka Tip Kur Tip Kha and Ka Kamai ia ka Hok. Greed, the mother of all evils, sat supreme in his heart, and in his craving for power and pelf, he trampled on the rights of others. He began to cheat, to swindle, to steal and even kill to gain what his avaricious heart desired. Respect for fellow men, through which alone Man could approach God, was completely forgotten, as men tried their best to outwit each other for the sake of wealth, their new god.

God, on his part, was greatly vexed by Man's rebelliousness. He was sorely grieved that Man had chosen to ignore and slight the covenant, and since this was quite meaningless now, He decided to break off his ties with Man and closed forever the Golden Ladder to Heaven through Sohpet Bneng. Away from the remaining Nine Clans in Heaven, and bereft of God's guidance and blessing, the Seven Clans remained helpless orphans on Earth, amidst a new kind of darkness that bred all sorts of evil in the minds of men. Their Golden Age had ended.

But where did this darkness come from? As evidence of His displeasure, God made an oak tree, situated on another sacred mount, grow day by day to a monstrous height and width, so that its shadow expanded to eclipse whole portions of the Earth in pitch darkness. The perpetual darkness caused by the branches of *Diengïei*, the name then given to this 'Tree of Gloom', made standing crops wilt and threatened to destroy all plant life, as well as making Man himself vulnerable, a prey to wild beasts and many other evils.

Man panicked. But as is characteristic of him, instead of first turning inwards to examine his soul, then conceding his own aberration and approaching God with a repentant heart, he proudly sought his own solution to the ever-worsening crisis that menaced his very existence.

He convened an extended council to which male representatives of all the Seven Clans were summoned. After hurried consultations, the council resolved to bring down Diengïei, which was even then enlarging itself alarmingly. In passing the resolution, the council declared:

'We do not know the cause of this terrible darkness, nor why Diengïei has suddenly grown so malevolently huge. But we need not seek the reason immediately. What we need to realize is that our very survival is threatened; we must act quickly and decisively. We must bring down this Tree of Gloom before its foul shadow destroys us. In order to do this, each family must send at least one man, equipped with a large knife and an axe, to carry out the task.'

Work on toppling Diengïei commenced immediately. The men chopped and hacked away from dawn to dusk, lopping off a bit of the trunk each day. But always, when they came back the next day, they found the tree whole again. It looked like it had never been touched.

The men were dumbfounded, and some of them grew apprehensive, for it seemed to them that the tree had mysterious powers. How could they fight something that could heal itself as soon as it was cut?

While they sat brooding, in fear and confusion, a little wren called Phreit came flying to the paddy fields nearby. The bird had never seen men in such gloom before, but on learning the cause, it offered to reveal the secrets of Diengïei:

'It is not what you think, O men. Diengïei may have the power to grow with the swiftness of a bird's flight, but it does not have the power to heal itself. I know its secrets and I'm ready to help should you wish me to. All that I ask is that you allow me to feed freely in your paddy fields so that I too may survive.'

By then the men were so thoroughly demoralized and desperate that they were prepared to listen to just about anyone with new ideas. Once the deal was struck, Phreit told them that it was not the magic powers of the tree that were responsible for its extraordinary recovery, but the licking of its trunk by the Tiger as soon as the men retired to their homes for the night. That was how the gashes filled up as fast as they were made.

The Tiger (a symbol of all that was evil and cruel) wanted Diengïei to stand, as the expanding eclipse caused by its growth made his hunting easier. In fact, he was looking forward to the time when the whole world was totally blanketed in darkness, so that he could then start preying on Man too. To foil the evil designs of the Tiger, Phreit advised the men to fortify the portion of the trunk that they had hewn by placing knives and axes against it each night.

Encouraged by this revelation, the men hustled back to the task, and at the end of their day's work, set their axes against the tree. The next morning, instead of a healed trunk, they discovered bloodstains on their axes and, later, they learnt that the Tiger had lapped his tongue to shreds, then, terrified, had fled the place for an unknown destination. They were elated. They fell upon the tree with fresh vigour and after some weeks found they had cut it down. Everyone heaved a sigh of relief.

The pact made with the little Phreit marked the first gesture of Man towards repentance and humility. And that was why God had granted Man success in felling the Diengïei.

---

[1]A reference to this can be found in the story of 'The Fight between Kyllang and Symper', the two most celebrated mountain spirits.

The Purple Crest

After the fall of Diengïei and the return of light to Earth, there was much rejoicing among Earth's inhabitants: men, animals, birds and all other living creatures. To celebrate the event, Man prepared a huge dancing ground and sent word to all forms of life on Earth announcing the dance he intended to organize. Man did not omit even heavenly beings like the Sun and the Moon from his invitation.

On the day of the festival, all manner of beings from all four corners of the globe converged upon the dancing ground; they enjoyed the day's festivities as only those could who had lived with so much suffering and so devoid of pleasure for so long. The Sun and the Moon arrived at the scene, however, only towards the end of the celebration. The Sun, on whose good offices depended the smooth running of everything in the universe, could not leave her work untended without first setting things in order. Not to attend the festival altogether would appear arrogant on her part, and she thought, therefore, that putting in an appearance would at least show her goodwill. That was why she and her brother, the Moon, went to the festival and danced on together even when all the others had abandoned the arena and were engaged in other forms of pleasure.

But the spectacle of the lone dancers created a tremendous uproar. The gathering, prominent in which were the Owl, the Mole, the Frog and the Monkey, began to ridicule and boo the latecomers.

'Look at those two clowns dancing alone on the empty grounds!' hooted the Owl.

Then the angry Mole shouted, 'You insolent hypocrites! If you don't want to dance together with the rest of us, why did you come at all?'

And then the Frog croaked out, 'You are too early for the next festival!'

But what hurt the heavenly sister and brother the most was the Monkey's nasty indictment. 'Hey, you two!' she shouted. 'Are you brother and sister or husband and wife that you are dancing so intimately together?'

The two could stand it no longer and left the field, vowing never to show their faces to the world again. The Sun, on whom the universe hinged, she, who was the queen of the heavens, felt especially stung by the unwarranted insults heaped upon her and her brother. 'You filthy, vicious creatures!' she raged. 'Is this how you treat your own guests! Is this the reason you have called us, so that you could humiliate us? In your beastly rudeness you have gone so far as to accuse us of abominable incest, you foul-tongued things! You will never see us in this dirty place again!'

Having hurled her tirade at the stunned gathering, the Sun went to hide herself in *Krem Lamet Krem Latang*, the Cave of the Sanctified Leaf, which was somewhere beyond the Valley of Death on the way to the House of God.

From that day the whole world was thrown once again into perpetual night. Man was stupefied. To experience a second darkness so soon after the harrowing first, filled him with dread, and there was much fear and shedding of tears among the other earthlings. Everyone was overtaken with remorse, and they called after the Sun and the Moon and prayed to them that they might return to light up the days of Earth. But all those cries and pleadings were in vain. The Sun and her brother could not forgive them so easily, and refused to be drawn back into the world.

When the initial shock and confusion had subsided, Man, who was more sensible than the rest of the beings, convened a council to choose someone from among them, someone with more than ordinary gumption and strength, to bring the Sun back into their midst. The first choice fell on the Elephant, the largest and strongest of them all. It was a choice that personified brute strength and reflected Man's pride in his own knowledge—and his short-sightedness in believing that the Sun, who signified heavenly light, could be intimidated by a show of force.

But the Elephant himself quaked at the mere thought of confronting the might of heavenly powers. He said, 'Hear me, O Man, my fellow creatures all, before you send me to my doom. I'm big and strong, there's no denying that. But going to the Cave of the Sanctified Leaf, I will have to go across rivers and seas, bogs and fens, and while crossing them, I fear my foreleg or my foot may get stuck. Demons may devour me; I may fall into pits and gorges and finally perish without achieving the task you have seen fit to bestow on me.

'Forgive me,' he urged. 'Let me off this impossible assignment, and I promise to give myself up to serving the interests of the council in every other way.'

After the Elephant had spoken his mind, there was a sudden hush in the gathering. All seemed affected by the simple truth of what he had said; they bowed their heads and did not offer to volunteer themselves.

But the Hornbill, cocksure and proud of his good looks and accomplishments, came forward and said, 'Listen to me, my friends, I will shoulder this responsibility. I will go to the Cave to fetch the Sun and the Moon. With me to plead for you, they won't be able to resist.'

When they heard this imperious utterance, there was much relief and joy among the crowd to know that there was at least one who dared face the dangers implied in the journey to the other world. All those present could not wait to give the Hornbill their heartiest congratulations.

True to his words, the Hornbill went to the Sun's hiding place, where he presented himself as the ambassador of the whole world, there to discuss her return to Earth. At first the Sun treated him with respect and hospitality; she gave him shelter and good food, as she would give any honoured guest in her house. But presumptuous and vain as he was, the Hornbill took her kindness for her weakness for him, and he began to court her—this ruler of the universe at whom no other creature would have dared even to look. Enraged, the Sun snatched up a golden stool and threw it with all her might at his beak. Shouting and cursing him all the while, she said, 'You shameless creature! From now on you will bear my golden stool wherever you go! You will be plagued with coughing and asthma, and you will fly sideways, trying to avoid my golden rays, all your life!'

It was with great humiliation that the Hornbill directed his way back to Earth. The councillors could hear his coughing and wheezing from far away, and they were all curious. Embarrassed and feeling small, the Hornbill recounted all that had happened to him—and from that day on he could never look straight at the Sun again.

Once more, there was crying and wailing throughout the land. And once more the same question was raised: 'Who will bring the Sun and the Moon back to Earth?' After what had happened to the Hornbill, however, no one felt bold enough to offer their services. Seeing no one come forward, Man inquired if there was anyone missing from the council. Soon, it was discovered that everyone was represented there except for the Rooster, who, they said, did not feel qualified to attend since he was—in those days—a featherless creature hugging the weeds and bushes, too scared of the other animals to venture out.

Then someone recalled that the Rooster had not attended even the dance festival, at which the whole gathering erupted into an uproar of angry shouts over how the Rooster had defied the entire council of creatures by ignoring an event it had organized. He must be punished, they said, he must be sent to the Cave or be responsible for all the evils and wrongs in the world—in other words, he must bring the Sun and the Moon back to Earth.

Man sent for the Rooster, ordering him to come to the council. In his turn the Rooster said, 'My Lord and fellow beings underneath the heavens, I'm prepared to go to the Cave of the Sanctified Leaf and expose myself to all sorts of dangers for your sake. I am also prepared to lose my neck for your faults and failings. But who am I to stand before such royal beings as the Sun and the Moon? I am only a desperate featherless wretch, lying low among small plants and dark holes. Now, if you can give me the forked and resplendent tail of the Skylark, if you can cloak me from head to foot in finery and warm feathers bright with all sorts of brilliant colours, I promise to give up my very life, willingly, for the sake of the general good. And if you promise to acknowledge my deeds throughout my life and to let me occupy a place of honour in all your rituals, I am ready to go at once.'

The council endowed him with all he had asked for, and on top of that it placed a purple crest on his head to make him look even more like an emissary fit to meet the gods.

On his way to the Cave, the Rooster met Jri, the Rubber Tree, whom he asked for shelter. But Jri said, 'There are demons living on my branches. They will devour you if you spend the night here.'

Undaunted, the Rooster replied, 'If you let me stay the night, when I return, if I have coaxed the Sun into relenting, I will let you share the role I have in the solemn rituals of Man.' Seeing that he was determined, Jri decided to allow him to sleep in a hole in its trunk.

The next night the Rooster met Sning, the Oak Tree, whom he also asked for a place to sleep, promising to keep a role for him in the religious ceremonies before the altar, when he was congratulated and thanked on his successful return from his mission. The Rooster also offered the same thing to Lamet, the Leaf, whom he met on the following night.

After he had travelled for many days and undergone much hardship on the way, the Rooster finally reached the retreat of the Sun, beyond the Valley of Death. It needed only one look at him for the Sun to see that here was no randy young fool like the Hornbill. She welcomed him gladly and treated him with great benevolence, giving him royal food and a royal bed for his rest. But in his humility the Rooster asked only for the leftovers of winnowed rice, which he said he would eat in the courtyard in front of her door, adding that he was only a poor desperate being, not deserving of such good things and royal treatment.

Impressed, the Sun said, 'Tell me, why did you come here?'

The Rooster answered, 'My Queen, O Mother, the whole world was thrown into darkness when you left for this Cave. Man, animals and all other creatures live in great anxiety and dread. Unless you come back, there will be no peace on Earth. Come back, O Mother, and I will stand accountable for all the injustices and transgressions of Man and his fellow creatures. It was their mistake not to think before they acted, not to limit their scorn to their own kind. But from now on, I will be answerable for all their wrongdoings, and I will see that no other outrage befalls you again. Before you peep into the world I will shake my shield and thrice will I sound my bugle, as signs that the world is fit for your divine blessing.

'Come, O Mother,' he ended his plea, 'for I have traded my life to be an intercessor with the gods, a redeemer of wrongs.'

Touched by the eloquence of one so simple and modest, the Sun could do no other than give him her assurance that she would return to Earth and forgive the misdeeds of all earthlings for his sake. Before she sent him away, she bestowed upon him the right to be the Pioneer who will open the way, the Pleader before God, and the negotiator between all things earthly and heavenly.

Thus the Rooster returned to Earth in triumph, and amidst a thunderous reception, the victorious fowl was awarded the title of U Saw Shyrtong, or the 'Purple Crest'. But glory did not make the Rooster forget that it was his humility, his self-abasement before the goddess that had carried the day for him. So he remembered his pledge to the Sun and when dawn came, he shook his shield and sounded his bugle, thrice, at regular intervals. And then, like the lifting of a veil, darkness was removed and light filtered into a world once more full of the joy of living.

Man kept his promise to the Rooster as well. To this day he never begins a ritual or a thanksgiving without the sacrificial blood of the Rooster placed before a piece of Jri, the Rubber Tree, Sning, the Oak Tree, and Lamet, the Leaf, the three to whom the Rooster had promised a share in the ceremonies.

The Lost Manuscript

After the felling of Diengïei,[1] and Man's violation of the covenant he had with U Blei, his Creator, that he would always live by His commands, God on his part broke off ties with him and closed forever the Golden Ladder to Heaven through Lum Sohpet Bneng. The closing of the Golden Ladder also signalled the end of the Golden Age in Man's history and thereafter followed a period of confusion, with Man becoming the victim of all sorts of evil practices and all kinds of superstitious fears, having lost the divine guidance of God.

Groping through that gloom, some of the more righteous elders remembered God and the happy life they had led under His guiding spirit. These convened a council of all mankind, where they impressed upon the members the need to enjoy the benefit of living under the divine commandments once more, so that their life would not be godless, and so that they would be better counselled in their day-to-day activities and their relationship with their fellowmen. They said:

'Do you remember the three commandments of U Blei, our God? How happy we were when we lived guided by those divine decrees, the foundation of our *aïom ksiar*, the Golden Age of our existence. Let us turn back to God, let this groping in the dark like blind men end here and now. Let us plead to God for mercy, and for signs of His mercy. Let us plead with Him for his spiritual guidance.'

Having heard this powerful appeal, the council was wholly impressed and pleaded with the elders to do whatever was necessary to bring God's benign presence back in their midst. The task of intervening with God was, therefore, left to the elders, and they immediately set to worshipping their Creator day and night till at last He was moved to pity and showed them signs, directing them to send an ambassador to meet Him on the summit of a tall mountain, along with a representative of the people called Dkhar, who lived in the plains below Ri Khasi, the land of the Khasis.

The two emissaries were sent to the mountain, where they met God and were given instructions for eight days and nights continuously about various rites and rituals, and especially about the ways of true and clean living. God also had the teachings, along with the alphabet of the scripts, recorded in a set of two documents and gave them to the two representatives so that they could better propound His laws to their people. He then sent them back home with careful instructions in regard to the safekeeping of the documents.

The two turned towards home in great excitement for they were taking to their people the laws of God himself with which they were determined to reform their societies of their many evil customs. But on the way, at the foot of the mountain, they encountered a critical problem in the form of a large river which was in flood. How could they make it to the other bank safely? More importantly, how could they make it with their treasures unspoilt? They knew well that contact with water would immediately destroy the delicate tissue on which the teachings were written. But at the same time, their exultant mood and the desire to be home to a hero's welcome as soon as possible, caused them to abandon the idea of waiting for the flood to subside. They decided to risk crossing the river there and then, trying to protect their precious cargo as best they could.

The Dkhar, who sported a long tuft of hair on his pate according to the custom of his people, attached his document securely to it and swam safely across without so much as a ripple of water touching the manuscript. Safely on the other side, he hastened to his people in the plains without another thought for the Khasi.

The Khasi, who had no such tuft, took his document between his teeth and began to swim. But being a hillman, unaccustomed to swimming in large rivers, he soon found himself floundering, with his head bobbing in and out of the water. In trying to save himself and gulping air through his mouth, he accidentally swallowed his document, which by then had been reduced to pulp. Overtaken with remorse at what he had done, he lost his fear of the river and struggled back to where he had struck out, and went directly to the mountain to plead with God once again. The loss of the manuscript was not his alone but also that of his people's, because their spiritual well-being depended on it. Unfortunately for him, and the Khasis, however, God was nowhere to be found, and the man had to return home empty-handed.

On reaching home, the errant ambassador recounted everything that had happened to a very disappointed people. The man would have been torn to pieces by the angry crowd if he had not quickly offered one solution, which was that he would teach the people what he had been taught by God, because he still remembered, he said, some of the most important instructions.

The same people who had made him their intercessor with God convened another council, where each person was instructed on the teachings of God and his divine laws. But not remembering all he had been told, the teacher simplified everything. And that is why the religious thought of the Khasis is not very complicated. The people at the council found the teachings quite easy to follow and imprinted them in their hearts to pass on to future generations by word of mouth. And it is that personalization of the teachings and the divine laws that makes the worship of God, in every Khasi household today, a very personal matter, taking place in the heart of each individual and not in any church or temple.

The basic concept of religion rests mainly on the three doctrines: ban Tip Briew Tip Blei, ban Tip Kur Tip Kha and ban Kamai ia ka Hok: to know Man, to know God, to know the maternal and paternal relations and to earn righteousness. First of all, Man must respect Man, his life and the life of all that is in Nature, as the equal creations of the one supreme God, U Blei. It is only when man has learnt to respect and love his fellow beings that he can learn to respect his God, the Creator, the Keeper. And respecting and loving God means respecting and loving all that is godly and good in the world. It follows from this, therefore, that Man lives in the world to earn righteousness and having so earned it, he then returns to his Maker when he dies. The Khasis call this return *leit bam kwai sha ïng U Blei*: going to take betel nut in the House of God.

It follows from this that the Khasi universe, as described by the messenger, is essentially a two-tier system, comprising *Ka Bneng* (Heaven) and *Ka Khyndew* (Earth). The Khasi has no concept of hell and words like *dujok, ka nurok ka ksew* (the accursed place of the dog) and *ka khyndai pateng ñiamra* (the nine stages of the underworld) which signify hell have been borrowed from Hindu and Greek mythologies. But that does not mean that a person who does not lead a good clean life on earth will get off without the punishment commensurate with his crime. The Khasi belief says such a person is denied partaking of the divine betel nut, and his *rngiew*, his anima, is condemned to roam the world as *ki ksuid ki khrei*, one of the accursed and malignant spirits.

The spirit world of the Khasis on the other hand is a three-tier system. At the head of this system is God, U Blei, the Creator, the Keeper, presiding in Heaven with all the spirits and men and women, who are not merely people departed from this world but men and women who belong originally to heaven as *ki khyndai hajrong* or the Nine Above. Below God, there are the spirits, *ki blei*, who are not simply the various manifestations of God, but constitute His representatives on earth. Roughly corresponding to the Christian angels, and being God's representatives, these spirits, like U Lei Shyllong in Hima Shyllong, or U Suitnoh in Hima Sohra, are sometimes worshipped separately by the people. After the representative spirits come the lesser spirits, *ki puri* or fairies. Among these again, there are two categories: the fair-skinned *purilieh* or *puriblei*, godly fairies, and the dark-skinned *puriksuid* or evil fairies. The evil fairies are also called simply *ki ksuid* or demons, who are again of various types and hierarchies.

---

¹See 'The Seven Clans'.

The Animal
Dance Festival

A long, long time ago, when animals were not the savages they are now, they are said to have lived in a peaceful community, fraternizing in one language. There was no hostility or quarrel between them; the Tiger did not hunt the Goat, the Lion waited on the Cow and the Elephant communed with the Ant...

In that paradise-like state, there lived three friends who never parted company—Shakyllia, a little bird, Diengkhied, the Porcupine and Risang, the Squirrel. One day, the three of them decided to go on a tour of the woods, hills and valleys, and while they went about this, they came upon a circular dancing ground, where humans used to celebrate their yearly spring festival. The three had once or twice been lucky enough to witness the celebrations. They had seen chaste maidens clad in silk and velvet, with twinkling ornaments, gliding in their slow and solemn dance round the centre of the ground, their gold and silver crowns glinting in the sun with each movement. And they had seen young men prancing in a ring, their silver swords—their beautiful silver swords—flashing and their spurs jingling, while around them stood a multitude of cheering and admiring onlookers. What a charming sight it had been!

The memory put them in a fever of excitement, and they immediately swore to do everything in their power to coax their kindred into organizing such festivals themselves. They were quite sure they would fare no less than the humans in their endeavour. In fact, with the variety of skills at each of their command, they could even better the human beings.

Back home, they unfolded their plan to their friends and tried to enthuse everyone with it with a lively display of their own brand of music. Shakyllia played a tune on his flute; Porcupine accompanied him on cymbals; and Squirrel beat away on his little drums. Soon, a crowd collected around them. Seeing how well the three played, and encouraged by finding such accomplished musicians in their midst, everyone present began to think seriously of the idea of holding an animal dance festival in the manner of mankind's celebration. The idea became especially popular with the young, who were continually seeking out new forms of pleasure and distraction.

A council was summoned to work out the various tangles of the novel project, and when everything was finally settled, the council selected one from among them who was young, energetic and wise, to be the chief organizer. The chosen youth was Pyrthat, the Thunder, who immediately made a massive drum and went about the animal kingdom beating it and booming out invitations to all fun-loving beasts to attend and participate in the biggest animal show on earth.

When the appointed day arrived, a huge and motley crowd converged upon the dancing ground, which the organizers had made ready after many moons of hard labour. Amidst hooting and laughter, they came from everywhere, crawling, walking, trotting, jumping or swinging from tree to tree, dressed in their own peculiar costumes and habits, their very best outfits. When the assembled crowd had taken their seats and the dancers had gathered in the field, the three friends (now accompanied by Hati, the Elephant, with his raucous trumpet) took up their instruments and proceeded to launch the festival. Following the music, the crowd erupted in a tremendous burst of applause, chanting praises and urging the dancers to give their finest performance.

Ka Shrieh, the Monkey, and her brood, emboldened by the continual promptings of the onlookers, let loose with their antics, screeching and making themselves a general nuisance to the other dancers by landing on their backs from time to time. Of course, they took the burst of laughter that followed to be due approval of their skill, and that only made them more vigorous. That day, they leapt around so much that they forgot from then on how to be still for any length of time.

Exasperated, U Kyrtong, the Wild Ox, blew through his nostrils, pawed the ground and shook his shaggy head, trying to get rid of the little monkeys that were clinging to his horns. He was so infuriated by their behaviour that he has never yet learned to be agreeable again. Close to him were some small animals, playing, and ki sniang, the boars, who were wrestling in the dust, oinking and patting each other with every throw they gave their fellow contestants.

In all that confusion it was ridiculous to see Ka Dkhoh, the Owl, imitating the maidens of the human race, shuffling through the sand, trying to look dignified, and staring into space. The Owl stared so hard and for so long, without batting her eyelids, that she became short-sighted and her eyes became big and round like marbles. When he noticed her, U Dkhan, the Mole, laughed himself silly, and continued to do so until his own eyes narrowed to the mere slits they are today. Needless to say, there was much fun and jollity during the festival. All sorts of animals, in all sorts of colours, did all sorts of things, so that it was impossible for even the most morose ones not to be excited. Members of the council joined in the revelry and impressed everyone with a lively exhibition of their art as the most able sword dancers in the arena. Among them were U Dngiem, the Bear, with his darkly sombre robes, U Sier, the Stag, with his many-branched antlers, U Labasa, the Leopard, and U Khla, the Tiger, with their beautifully adorned garments. The only animals who felt slightly disadvantaged by all that carousing were the musicians, for between the persistent uproar from the spectators and the din created by the performers, they were having a tough time making themselves heard.

In the heat of all that excitement U Kui, the Lynx, arrived clothed from head to foot in a brightly striped costume. On arriving, he staggered onto the dancing ground, produced a stunningly beautiful, dazzlingly radiant silver sword, and began strutting around the circle. Not one animal present failed to turn his head towards Lynx. They had never seen such a sword before. It flashed at every twist and turn Lynx made and seemed to defy the sun itself in its brilliance. No one could help admiring Lynx and his silver sword. The attention he was getting from the crowd turned his head and made him arrogant, more so with each passing moment, so that he began to think that without him the whole show would have collapsed. Hearing his vaunts, Thunder was deeply stung and, biding his time, he silently vowed to put Lynx in his place before the festival ended.

As soon as Lynx had taken a break, Thunder approached and requested him, 'My good friend, I have left my own sword at home and have nothing with me but my big drum. Would you please lend me your magnificent sword for a moment? I would love to try my hand at sword dancing.'

Lynx looked sullenly at him and said rudely, 'If you want to participate in the sword dance you should have known better than to come to the field without your sword. Why don't you just go back home and fetch it?'

But some of the animals who were sitting nearby overheard the conversation and condemned Lynx for his selfishness. 'Shame on you, Lynx,' they said in a chorus, 'how could you be so ungracious? If it had not been for Thunder here, there would not have been a dance at all.' These animals also threatened that if Lynx did not lend his sword to Thunder, they would take it from him by force. Lynx did not want to part with his precious sword; for one thing he did not want anyone else to handle it, and for another, he especially did not want Thunder to get hold of it lest he dance better and win all the praise. In the face of this threat, however, he really had no option.

Taking the sword, Thunder went to the centre of the circle and beat on his drum to attract attention. When all eyes were on him, he began chanting as swordsmen used to do, and with a sudden motion and the speed of a whirlwind, he pranced round and round, furiously brandishing the sword, here, there and everywhere, so that it seemed, to the whole throng, like one mad, vengeful stick of pure flame, blinding anyone who so much as opened his eyes. The animals were alarmed. And then Thunder began to beat his drum with such force that the whole surrounding area shook as though a mighty tremor had occurred. Frightened out of their wits, the animals went on a rampage and fled to nearby jungles to hide in the undergrowth.

Amidst all that chaos, Thunder, who was so enamoured of the sword, which had given him such power, vaulted into the sky, far beyond the reach of Lynx and the other animals. And to this day he is often seen wildly striking the sky with what we have come to know as thunderbolts. Actually, these phenomena are nothing but the gigantic drum of Thunder and the silver sword of Lynx, metamorphosed into elemental forces.

On earth the confusion still prevailed, with each animal blaming the other for what had happened. However, no one was as sad as Lynx, who spent his days moping and seeking out ways to reach the aerial dwelling of Thunder so that he might recover his sword. Finally, he hit upon a simple but unique plan. First, he dug a small hole in the ground as foundation. Then he went to relieve himself in it everyday, hoping that one day the mound would grow as high as the sky. That is why Lynx never strays far from where he is staying, because to this day, he continues to build his mound in this way.

When the story of how Lynx had lost his rare silver sword came to be known by the humans, they felt sorry for him. As a token of respect for this great sword dancer, they decided never to disturb his habitat in any way so that he would be free to continue with his efforts to reach the sky.

Luri Lura, the Animal Fair:

How the Dog Came to Live with Man

In the days when the world was still young, when all animals lived together in peace and spoke the same language, they used to have fairs and markets where they bought and sold merchandise, just as Man did. The most prominent of such fairs was held in the forest area of Ri Bhoi, adjoining what is now called the state of Assam. This fair was called 'Ka Ïew Luri Lura', or the Luri Lura Fair, after the pandemonium and disorder that prevailed therein towards the end.

Every fair day, animals of all sorts and sizes from all over the land went to Luri Lura with their individual merchandise to trade and barter with one another. The Tiger, whom everyone feared and respected, was elected governor, to see that things ran smoothly within the fairground. And so everything went well. The fair prospered and more animals came to patronize it, each trying to add to its variety and glamour in his or her way. The Bear, for instance, would bring her honeycombs, the Monkey her fruits and the Deer her *amla*, to exchange with the herbs and plants and foodstuffs of other beasts.

Only the Dog never had anything to sell. He spent most of his time at the fair nosing about for scraps of food the others chanced to drop. When, eventually, he became a little ashamed of his habit, he determined to look for something he could call his own, something novel to offer. After days of wandering through the countryside, he suddenly came upon a basketful of leaf packets containing bean sauce, a delicacy for humans called *tung rymbai*, left hidden by some traders on their way to their own market, perhaps because they found it too burdensome to carry.

The Dog began to sniff about the strange substance. The odour was strongly redolent of Man's excrement, and as the Dog had once or twice dined on Man's excrement before and liked it, he presumed the other animals would also find the black pulpy mass a rare and appetizing treat to supplement their daily diet. Very pleased with his discovery, he walked off with it to the fair at Luri Lura.

There he stationed himself at the most prominent point in the centre of the fair and began howling and baying at the top of his voice, extolling the virtues of his stock and inviting all the animals to taste for themselves the only thing of its kind in the marketplace. Curious about the strange and reputedly delicious food the Dog had discovered, they all scampered to his side. 'What is it? What are you selling? Let us see,' they asked in one voice.

Feeling important and excited at the attention he was

attracting, the Dog promptly uncovered his basket and prepared to do business. But no sooner had he done this than a horrible stench issued from the basket, suffocating everyone present. 'It stinks! It stinks!' they all cried. 'What is this you have come to sell in our market?' Maddened by what they took to be the Dog's malignant trickery, believing that he was trying to con them in the most shameful manner, they began to chase him out of the fair, trampling underfoot his basket of tung rymbai. The Dog barked, howled, yelped, protested and argued with them till the whole fair resounded with the din. But their animal passions were truly roused and there was no reasoning with them.

In all that commotion and chaos, the Tiger arrived, muscling his way into the melee to investigate and seek out the cause of it all. The Dog voiced his complaints—but the Tiger had also been smothered by the same fetid smell. 'What is this!' he roared. 'How dare you defile our marketplace, selling Man's dung? If you don't leave this very minute, I will swallow you whole!' Terrified and humiliated, the Dog slunk away from Luri Lura amidst sneers and guffaws, catcalls and boos, which rankled in his mind long after they could be heard no more.

As a last resort, the Dog approached Man, to appeal for justice and succour. 'My Lord,' he said, 'you who are wise, who know and understand many things, do you think it is proper for the animals to trample on the rights and property of a weak and helpless creature like myself?' Man realized that the Dog had been greatly wronged, but he was powerless in the matter. 'How can I, as Man,' he said, 'judge the affairs of animals?'

Nevertheless, the Dog continued to plead with him. His own kind had turned their backs on him—worse, they had banished him from their midst. He was all alone in the world, and friendless; everyone would tyrannize him. He begged

Man to be his master, to allow him to live close to his house. He would protect the house and be Man's watchdog wherever he went. He also promised to do anything for Man and asked in return for only food and shelter and a chance to avenge himself upon his tormenters.

As he listened to the Dog's desperate pleas, Man could not help sympathizing. After all, here was another fellow sufferer, a creature of God like himself. He agreed to the Dog's entreaties—and that was how the Dog became Man's most beloved friend, accompanying him everywhere, but especially to the hunting grounds where he took grim pleasure in nosing and noisily forcing animals out of their lairs. And he was very good at that, for the tenacious scent of his tung rymbai that had clung to their cloven feet after Luri Lura, persisted with them and was passed on to their descendants.

The Peacock and the Sun

It was said that in the beginning, when the world was very young, the Peacock and the Sun lived together in heaven as husband and wife. And theirs was a paradise of warmth and love, a fairyland of never-ending joy—until one clear winter morning when the Sun, sovereign of the universe, was alone in the sky, unveiling marvellous scenes and faraway lands. While the Sun was thus busy presiding over the affairs of heaven and earth, distributing warmth, light and vitality to all sorts of beings, the Peacock, her husband, was languidly strolling about his celestial garden, which darkness never touched and where birds sang continuously to ever-blooming orchids.

Then his eyes turned to the distant lands on earth revealed to him by the unveiling rays of his wife. There he saw, dancing on the plains, what seemed to him to be a virgin queen, displaying her yellow and green royal robes in the morning light. The Peacock had heard of these beautiful humans living on earth, and he thought she must be the loveliest among them.

'Ah, what a woman, what a beautiful woman!' he said to himself. Surely she must be more exciting than his wife, who never seemed to have enough time to sit back and enjoy life with him. As he gazed and gazed and wondered, a terrible madness gripped his soul and shook him with a strange emotion. 'Such beauty! Surely I must go to her!' he soliloquized. 'Who could she be; whose daughter or granddaughter could she be?'

Without so much as an explanation to his wife, the Peacock announced his intention to leave her and descend into what he thought was another heaven of beautiful women. The Sun wept, failing to make him understand what it really was like down on earth. She dissolved into imploring tears that only fell on his tail, never touching his heart. Had she loved too much? Pampered him too much, so that he was suffering from a surfeit of vanity? The Sun could not understand, and kept on trying to hold on to him, crying all the while. And as she cried, more of her golden tears fell on his tail, making spotted patterns all over it.

Finally, the Peacock wrested himself free from her embrace and began his descent.

But what could he find on earth that was not in heaven? Instead of the welcoming smiles and outstretched arms that he had seemed to have been promise, he only found a vast rolling field of mustard plants, their yellow blooms flirting with the wind and laughing in his face.

The distance had deceived him. The dancing virgin

queen was none other than the mustard plants blowing in the wind.

Now it was his turn to cry. 'Alas, what a fate!' he lamented. Memories of the nectar-filled days of his life with his wife kept coming to eat his heart out, mocking his soul and torturing him. 'I will go back,' he resolved. 'Surely I will find a welcome!'

Looking at him from the heavens, the Sun wept afresh for him. She longed to take him back but then her earlier tears had been shed for a deeper reason than a husband's infraction, for she knew that it was beyond her power to accept or reject him now. How could he ever aspire to heaven again, having violated the divine word that made him and the Sun husband and wife? How could he ever make it to the celestial realms, burdened now with a treacherous heart?

The Peacock tried, and is still trying. Early, every sunshiny day, he is seen strutting about and leaping up and down, trying to get back to heaven and his beloved wife. But of course he cannot make it more than a few feet off the ground.

That was how the world became the restless Peacock's home. And that was how his loving wife's ethereal tears became the spotted glory of his tail and marked the memories of a heaven lost forever.

Death in a Hut:

The Story of the Betel Nut, the Betel Leaf, the Lime and Tobacco

This is a tale of friendship, the most ennobling kind of friendship, a story of two men, each of whom would rather have died than hurt the feelings of the other.

It all began a long time ago, when the world was still in a state of innocence, when no discrimination was known between the rich and the poor. During that time there lived, in a small and ancient Khasi village called Rangjyrwit, two great and loving friends, U Nik Mahajon, a rich bachelor, and U Shing Raitoi, a poor man with a poor wife, ironically called Ka Lak, meaning 'great wealth'.

The love between the two friends was a very strange one by

present-day standards. From the point of view of material wealth, they had nothing in common. Nik Mahajon, who was a prosperous merchant, never lacked anything in his life. Shing Raitoi, on the other hand, was a mere labourer, who had to cut wood, break stones and do all sorts of odd jobs just for a handful of rice each day. But his rich friend never looked down on him. He respected Shing Raitoi and treated him as he would an equal. Often, he invited his poor friend to his house, and whenever Shing visited him, Nik Mahajon never let him go away empty-handed, but always gave him something useful to carry back home. Shing was by no means a covetous man, but however hard he tried to say no to these gifts, his rich friend simply would not hear of it.

This state of affairs continued for a long, long time and quite troubled poor Shing, who realized how one-sided things were. Every time he returned from a visit he never failed to discuss things with his wife as to how to repay his friend for his goodness. Eventually, the couple decided to forget their shame and invite Nik to their place at least once, in spite of the bareness of their home and the emptiness of their larder.

So, one day, Shing went over to the rich man's house and said to him: 'My dearest friend, Nik, I have been here so many times, but my home has never even seen your shadow.' Jokingly, he added, 'Is it that you dislike witnessing my poverty?'

'Why do you say that, my dearest Shing,' Nik replied, 'when I have always wanted to visit you at your home to see what kind of things you do to spend your spare time, and perhaps enjoy a meal with you?'

'If that is how you feel,' replied Shing, 'you must surely drop by at my humble dwelling one of these days. I hope it doesn't matter to you if we can provide only a simple dish of rice and salt.'

To this meek submission, Nik said, 'Surely not, my friend! When the heart is loving, anything tastes good.'

So pleased was Shing with this assurance that he left his friend's house without even waiting to finalize the date of Nik's visit to his own home. Perhaps, if he had not overlooked this, the ensuing tragedy would not have happened at all.

Some time after this, Nik called on Shing for the first time in his life. Shing and his wife were pleased with their kind friend's graciousness, and received him as only true and loving hearts like theirs could. After a brief exchange of pleasantries, Lak left the two men to themselves, to enjoy their get-together according to their liking, while she went to the kitchen to busy herself with her own chores.

Having basked for some time in the glory of his friend's only visit, Shing thought it was fit and proper for him to entertain Nik with whatever food they had in the house. Excusing himself for a moment, he went to the kitchen and asked his wife to prepare something for all of them, so they could enjoy dinner together. He was determined that his friend should not leave his house without something to eat, partly because of his love for him and partly because he did not want him to think that he was mean.

It was with great shock and dismay, therefore, that he learned from his wife that there was not a morsel of food in the house, not even rice enough for one person.

What was he to do? His beloved friend was visiting his house for the first time, and he could not even treat him to a simple dinner! What a shame, he thought, what a horrible disgrace! 'Go, my dear wife, go to our neighbours and borrow some rice, so that we may at least feed our dear friend. Only enough rice to boil for a single meal, just that. That is all we need.'

The faithful Lak went round the village asking for the rice, but all the neighbours, who were as poor as Lak and her husband, either proved to be as empty of provisions, or distrusting of their capacity to return the handout. They banged their doors closed on her and Lak came back home in deep gloom to tell her husband how hopeless the errand had turned out to be. Hearing this, and unable to go back to his friend, whom he had left alone in the other room since he learned of the disgraceful predicament, Shing suddenly snatched up a carving knife hanging nearby. Declaring to his wife, 'It is better to die than to live in such humiliation,' he stabbed himself in the very heart and died there and then.

Lak stood there, a dumb witness to her dearest love's desperate deed. His death seemed as sudden and shocking as when her neighbours, unmoved by her plight, had slammed their doors on her. Then she slowly came back to herself and thought of her life. How full of hardship and privation her whole existence had been! And now that her only faithful companion, her husband, had also deserted her, she did not think life worth living any more. 'What will I do alone in this wretched world of grief and suffering, of shame and disgrace? As I lived with him, so shall I die with him!' And so saying, she wrested the knife from her husband's breast and killed herself with it.

While the horrifying scene was being enacted in the kitchen, the sanctum sanctorum of Khasi homes, Nik was getting more and more bored and fidgety alone in the sitting room. He could not understand why his good friend should suddenly disappear and leave him to his own company. It was so unlike him, and in Khasi manners, it was not at all polite. In fact, it was an outright insult to neglect a guest. But Nik knew his friend too well to condemn his behaviour without knowing the first and the last of it. Therefore he got to his feet, resolutely, to see for himself what was happening in the kitchen.

The first things he saw there were the bodies of his friend and his beloved wife, and the blood that flooded the room. Nik was dumbfounded. After such a happy time together, what could have driven his friend to cut short his own life like this! That the two had taken their own lives he was in no doubt at all. All the evidence pointed to that. But the motive! What could have been the motive?

After inspecting the almost bare and bloodied room, he noticed a rice pot boiling in the fireplace with nothing but water in it. 'Ah!' he exclaimed. 'Oh, my Creator, my Keeper! Now I know! But why, friend, why? Just because you couldn't feed me? As if I ever expected anything but love from you! What are all my possessions to me now? I have lost the best wealth I ever had. Let me die here with you!' And with these words, he also seized the knife, stabbed himself and fell dead on the spot.

Oblivious of the tragedy that had befallen the house of Shing, the Rooster, herald of the Sun, sounded his first bugle of the day, announcing the approach of dawn. His crowing caused a roving thief, who was running past the house, great alarm. He had been trying all night to flee his pursuers from a nearby village. With the coming of dawn so soon, where would he hide? The open house, which had been just a little time ago such a happy dwelling for two very poor, but very loving souls, appeared deserted. It must be an abandoned house, he thought, stealing into it to hide and rest for a while. But because he was so tired and spent, he found his eyes closing against his will, opening only when it was bright morning and most people were about.

Rubbing his eyes, he looked about the place which he had stumbled into and which he thought had saved him from sure punishment. But when he saw the dead bodies and the inundation of blood, he jumped up as if bitten by a snake and called out, for the first time in his adult life, the name of his mother. 'Wow Mei,' he shouted. 'What doom is this for me! From the mouth of the Tiger into the jaws of the *Thlen* ! [1] If people find me here, they will take me not only for a thief, but a murderer, a blood-hunter. What shall I do? Alas, there is no peace for the soul that is black!'

Having quite exhausted himself cursing his own fate, he began to think seriously of his predicament. He knew, for instance, what awaited him if he was caught. First, the three-patterned shaving of his head. Then the parade through the village, with the crowd beating at the drums tied to his back, for all to know that he was a killer. And finally, of course, *u tangon u lymban*, the heavy logs with which to break his neck.

'To die after having gone through so much humiliation,' he thought, 'and that too for no fault of my own! I would rather die now, a clean, honourable death along with these unhappy people.' And so he grasped the very same weapon and ended his thieving career for ever.

When the villagers came to know about the terrible tale, they were moved as they had never been moved before. The same gruesome fate could overtake any one of them, they reflected, and any of those who could not repay their more fortunate neighbours with the same act of kindness. They called a council of the whole village and prayed to their Creator, U Blei, to devise new ways of exchanging pleasantries and gifts, and to make new things, and create eatables that were easier to procure than rice, so that such a tragic event might never again be experienced when a poor man was visited by a rich friend.

God, who was just and kind and who saw everything, created, from the four bodies lying in the hut, a betel nut tree, a betel leaf plant, lime and tobacco, so that the rich and the poor might commune and extend hospitality to each other without the necessity of making rice or tea. It was from then that the custom of exchanging *kwai*, or betel nut, taken together with betel leaf, lime and sometimes tobacco, started among the Khasis. Nik Mahajon, who was a rich man, metamorphosed into a betel nut, Shing Raitoi and his wife Lak became a betel leaf and lime, which are taken together, and the thief turned into tobacco, which the Khasis insert in the corner of their mouths, as if to provide it with a hiding-place.

---

[1]Man-eating serpent.

Ka Nam and the Tiger

*O*ne hot and sultry day a woman, who was many months into her pregnancy, suddenly developed an intense yearning for lemon, or anything sour to quench her terrible thirst. As there was no one at home, and as she could find nobody to get the lemons for her, she decided to venture into the nearby forest to look for them herself.

Having gone deep into the forest, she came upon a large tree laden with small sour-sweet fruits that the Khasis call *sohphie*. Seeing these, she became mad with desire. But how could she, a woman big with child, get at them? How could she climb so tall and so big a tree? Looking at the fruit with her mouth watering and her eyes tearful, she exclaimed in her misery. 'Ah! If only there was someone to shake the tree or pluck the fruits for me! I'd give him anything in my power.'

Hearing that, the Tiger, who was dozing on the branches under the thick leaves of the tree, away from the blazing sun, looked down and roared out his reply, 'If you promise to give me what I will ask from you, I will throw down these fruits to you.'

Startled by the deep-throated voice, the woman looked up, to see none other than the dreaded Tiger. But, tormented by her craving, the woman forgot her fear for the moment and pleaded with the Tiger to pass a few sohphie down to her so that she could return home with her thirst quenched. She added that it was not auspicious for a gestating woman to be denied her desire. Not getting what she wanted, she said, would surely affect the baby in the womb.

But the Tiger was unmoved. He reminded her of the cruel trick her kind had played on him, trying to cut out his very tongue while they were felling the Diengïei.[1] He also told her of his vow to avenge himself by killing and devouring any human that he met for what they had done to him. So nothing but her promise to give him whatever he would ask would save her and persuade him to help her get the fruits she desired.

The woman was silent for some time, and thought hard. 'If I shake my head at his demand,' she mused, 'he will surely kill me. On the other hand, if I say yes to whatever he asks, I will not only be saved, but also get the fruits. And once out of this forest and his grasp, how is he ever to find me again to force his demand on me?' And so she said, 'All right, my lord, I agree to your condition so long as it does not endanger my life in any way.'

Pleased with her words, the Tiger took hold of the tree and shook it with all his might so that the fruits came tumbling down like the hails of *Iaiong*, the black month of thunderstorms. Then the woman picked them up one by one, collected them in her apron and ate to her heart's content. The Tiger watched the woman enjoying the fruit with a mischievous twinkle in his eyes and a smirk on his lips. When she had done her eating, he reminded her of her promise. In a voice as loud as a thunder clap, he spelled out his sinister desire and said, 'Now that you have taken my fruits, you must keep your pledge. I see that you are two-bodied, and about to give birth to your child.... My wish is this: if it is a boy, he may be yours, but if it is a girl, she must be mine.'

Stunned, the woman gaped at him as he glided gracefully away. There was so much beauty in his movements, and yet so much cruelty in his heart. However, she soon took consolation from the thought that he would probably never see her again once she was back in the human world.

One night, some time after the frightening incident in the forest, the woman began to experience her birth pangs. As was the custom at such times, many of her friends and neighbours went to her house carrying flambeaux called *dongmusa* with them, to light their way. The Tiger, who had discovered the woman's dwelling place through his own initiative, and who had been spying on it all the while from the outskirts of the village, noticed the women with their dongmusa and instantly guessed that the time had come for the woman to deliver her child. So he stole to the house and lay in wait beneath it. After what seemed an agonizing eternity to him, the sound of an infant crying and the voices of several people shouting, 'A baby girl! A baby girl!' were heard. The Tiger, who had been very attentive, was overwhelmed with joy to think that the infant would soon be his. He began to laugh silently, beating his breast with pleasure. But just then he heard another chorus of voices shouting, 'Oh no! It's a boy after all!' That so upset him, that he turned tail and returned to his lair with a gloomy face, brooding on his own bad luck.

On his way back he met the Fox, whom he despised. He would have walked on without a word but for the Fox stopping him with a greeting, referring to his dark and sombre look. So great was his grief that the Tiger automatically found himself relating the whole story to the Fox. When he had heard the Tiger out, the Fox said, 'Why do you worry about such a small thing, my master? I often make forays into the village, picnicking on the villagers' poultry and sometimes their goats. If you allow me and are so kind as to trust me, I will find out for you if the baby is a boy or a girl. You see, tomorrow they will name the baby, for that is what they used to do a day after a child was born. If that is indeed what they still do, this time, I will go to the village and find out somehow if it is a boy's or a girl's name they give to it.'

The Tiger's face broke into a smile again. 'Do that,' he said, 'and I will reward you with a big plump goat'.

When morning came, the woman's friends, neighbours and relatives from far and near came flocking to her house for the naming rites. They took out their wooden mortars to pestle the best variety of rice, after which the flour, together with the purest beer kept in a gourd, were taken to the priest waiting in the *nongpei*, the front room of the house, for the ceremony. Meanwhile, a pig and chickens were slaughtered as a big feast was being prepared for the event, to the delight of one and all—and the greater delight of the stray dogs that swarmed around the place like the most welcome of guests.

Watching them, the Fox, who had been hovering around, thinking of a way to get nearer, immediately saw his chance. He sneaked in among them, made friends and mixed freely with them, so that it would have been impossible for anyone to distinguish him from the rest of the dogs, even if anyone had been interested in the distinction on such a happy occasion. That way the Fox was able to take care of both his stomach and his errand, from which he expected an even greater reward.

That night the Fox went to report to the Tiger and revealed that the baby's name was Ka Nam, a girl's name. On learning how he had been betrayed by the woman, the Tiger became so furious that he roared and tore many trees around him to shreds, pronouncing the most dreadful threats as he did so. The spectacle even frightened the poor Fox, who thought it best to leave and come back for his reward another day. As for the Tiger, he growled all night, vowing a terrible vengeance on the woman and her child.

The next day, however, he calmed down and thought it best to wait and bide his time. If the woman refused to hand over the child to him, there was nothing to do but to try to steal her. From that day the Tiger resumed his spying on the house, and when Nam grew into a plump and beautiful girl, he began to watch her movements very closely, stalking her and waiting for his chance.

Days flew by, became months and then years. The moon witnessed many changes of seasons in his wanderings, but things did not change with the Tiger, who nursed his vengeance with resolve. Meanwhile, the mother of Nam nursed her with loving and tender care so that she grew into a girl so attractive as to be a cause of jealousy to many a mother in the village.

The Tiger watched all this from a distance. He noticed, for instance, how Nam's soot-black hair reached her ankles; how her face shone and her eyes sparkled with such beauty that he was almost afraid to look straight into them; but most of all he noticed how graceful her movements were, and how her body had begun to fill out. 'Most delightful!' he thought to himself. He was sure that with a little more grooming she would grow up into a ravishingly beautiful young woman. All this made him resolve all over again to carry her away with him while she was still young and easy to handle. The proper care, to make her even more plumply appealing, he could manage on his own, without any further help from her parents.

Nam's mother had not forgotten the Tiger either, and although she was not unduly worried about him, she thought it best to advise her daughter of his threats. She asked Nam to take care where she went, and especially exhorted her not to venture too far from home when there was no one about. As might be expected of a young girl, Nam learnt to fear the Tiger and never played anywhere beyond the boundary of her courtyard. Gradually, her fear preyed so greatly on her mind that she never even accompanied her friends to the spring, gushing from a bamboo spout, situated only a stone's throw away from the last house of the village.

Seeing how cowardly Nam had become, her friends never missed a chance to taunt and ridicule her, especially when she refused to join them whenever they went to fetch water from the spring. Sick of these taunts, one day Nam decided to put a stop to them once and for all, and so, against the injunction of her mother, she took out the bamboo tubes, the cone basket and cane rope, and proceeded with her friends to the spring.

The Tiger, who was observing all this from the fringe of the forest, rushed to the spring, snatched Nam from among her friends and fled with her to his cave deep in the forest. It was all done so quickly that the little girls did not even have time to cry out, and when they later reported the matter to the village folk, the girls said all they saw was a flash of stripes and yellow, and the next thing they knew was that Nam was no longer with them.

When they heard what had happened, the parents cried

their hearts out, stopping only when the elders consoled them, saying that it was probably the will of God that Nam should seek out her own destiny, for, they said, Nam had been too exceptional a child to live out her life in the village like other girls. Even her name, meaning 'glory', had been blessed by God himself, and so, they said, it was possible that Nam would not die at the hands of the Tiger, but would live on to prove her glory to the world.

Meanwhile, in the cave of the Tiger, Nam was surprised to find him almost as gentle and affectionate as her parents had been. He gave her whatever she wanted, brought her whatever she asked for, and dressed her up like a princess. Everything was so unlike what she had heard about him from her mother that she quickly lost her dread of him and lived happily with him as the keeper of his den, till at last she grew up into a very fetching young woman.

As he watched her grow up, the Tiger too became even more caring of her. But Nam did not know that the Tiger was observing her the way a farmer would regard his prize pig, ready for the market, reluctant to part with it, yet thrilled at the very thought of the imminent sale. Thus, when one day the Tiger cajoled her with kind words to clean the den, and be ready to prepare for a big feast that he and his friends were planning to hold that evening, she did not in the least suspect that she would be the object of that feast. She did not suspect, that is, until a little Mouse whispered the terrifying secret in her ear.

It was quite by accident that Nam met the Mouse. Nam was busy cleaning the Tiger's dwelling and tidying things up according to the wishes of the Tiger, whom she had come to consider as her adopted father, when she noticed the Mouse nibbling away at some of the food she had cooked for the evening feast.

'Get away from there, you naughty little thing!' she shouted at her. 'Don't you see I'm preparing a feast?'

The Mouse scurried away from there, but before she ducked into her hole, she said, 'If you don't allow me to eat a little of the food, I will not tell you what I know about you.'

'What do you know about me?' demanded Nam.

'Something to do with your life,' the Mouse replied, evasively.

Her curiosity fully aroused now, Nam hastened to give the Mouse some food in exchange for her secret. Not very trusting by nature, the Mouse took care that she ate her fill of what Nam offered her, before parting with her information. And then she said, 'Your life is in grave danger. The Tiger whom you think loves you so much is right now collecting his friends together to feast on *you*, not on those pots of food you have cooked. His tenderness for you was only an excuse to keep you contented so you would grow faster and become more fetching for his appetite. In other words, he was merely fattening his sacrificial goat.'

Shocked beyond words, Nam stared at the Mouse in dumb amazement for a long time. She wished she could laugh in the creature's face and call her a nasty liar, but staring at her in open-mouthed silence, she realized the little creature was telling the truth. There was no reason for the Mouse to lie. Besides, in spite of all his apparent kindness to her, she knew, as everyone else did, that her substitute father was really a cruel bully who was feared and hated by everyone. Therefore, dazed and shaken, she asked her little saviour in a small and piteous voice, 'What am I to do?'

The Mouse thought for a moment and then smiled like someone who has made a great discovery. And so she had, for she presently said, 'I have a solution for you. First, of course, you must leave this cave at once and disguise yourself in a toad skin to avoid detection. Then we shall see about the rest.'

Immediately, the two left the cave and approached Hynroh, the Great Toad, who lived in a distant corner of the forest, in order to beg for a toad skin large enough to fit Nam from head to foot. It was not without fear that they went to her den, for Hynroh was known throughout the forest for her magical and malignant powers. In fact, it was said that her powers were so great that she had once or twice even done battle with heavenly beings.

As could be expected, Hynroh was secretly gloating that Nam had been compelled to come to her. She had heard of the girl's great beauty before. She had even gone to see the girl for herself once, and had been unreasonably envious of the fame that Nam's beauty had fetched her. She was therefore pleased to turn her into an ugly toad and—at Nam's own request, as it were—eclipse her beauty forever. She readily agreed to provide Nam with a toad skin, but also exacted her word of honour never to remove it for as long as she lived. The Toad also warned Nam not to venture out of the forest unless she wanted to incur the Toad's terrible wrath.

Seeing herself trapped into a toad's life under the control of the evil Hynroh, Nam began to weep bitterly. But then her companion soon calmed her down again by saying that she knew of a way out of her unenviable situation. As she spoke, the Mouse took Nam to the magic Kya and Jri, the cotton and rubber trees, and taught her the magic words: 'San, san Kong A, pat, pat Kong Ri; San, san Kong Ri pat, pat Kong A' or 'Grow, grow, Kong A, wait, wait, Kong Ri; grow, grow, Kong Ri, wait, wait, Kong A'. The chanting of these would make the two trees grow tall as the heavens and would thus take Nam to the realm of the Moon, the Stars and the Sun, away from the reach of evil creatures like the Tiger and Hynroh.

Following the instructions of the Mouse, Nam climbed

on to the branches of the trees, chanted the magic words, and away she went, up and up until she passed through the blue rock of heaven, through a secret passage, and reached the realm of heavenly beings, where she alighted to her new-found freedom. The little Mouse, who had been watching the spectacle, wiped away the tears streaming from her eyes—she had grown fond of Nam—and headed back to her hole in the cave.

Alone in the strange but beautiful country, Nam initially found relief and a sense of freedom. But as she wandered aimlessly about, she began to feel lonely and lost. When night came, her vague sense of loss became a sharp, biting anxiety. She hurried to the first palace she came across, to ask for shelter for the night. Approaching the palace, she noticed that its courtyard and surroundings were covered with a fine ash-like substance. The palace itself gave out a vague glow and also seemed to be painted with ash. It turned out that the palace belonged to the Moon, a handsome young god who adored beauty more than anything else in the heavens. When this worshipper of beauty heard someone knocking at his door, he asked his housekeeper to see who it was, but on hearing that it was only a hideous toad, he ordered her off his premises.

More worried now, Nam wandered off towards the mansion of the Evening Star, but there too she was refused shelter because she was so ugly. Disconsolate, she moved from palace to palace in search of lodging. In that heavenly realm, however, there seemed to be no place for someone as horrid-looking as a toad. Desperate, Nam thought of removing her toad skin and showing everyone that she was as lovely as the most elegant of them all. She had no fear of the Tiger any more, for she knew that she was beyond his reach, but she was in great dread of Hynroh, knowing that the sky was no limit for her magical powers. Already she had broken her promise to the evil creature not to leave the jungle, and so she did not care to incense her further by shedding her toad skin. She was thus left with no option but to roam about the heavens for weeks in her ungainly costume, hoping against hope that some kind soul might take pity on her plight.

It was in this way that she finally arrived at the dazzling palace of the Sun. As usual, Nam requested the Sun to allow her to live in the palace as a lodger; but the Sun, like the rest of the inhabitants of that celestial land, could not bear to look on someone as ghastly as a woman who so closely resembled a revolting toad. She was about to send the girl away when Nam fell at her feet and said, 'My benefactress, Queen of the Universe! I have been tramping about for God knows how many days now without a roof over my head. No one has been kind enough to give me shelter, even for one night. If you, a woman, a queen, refuse to help another woman like me, then what will be my fate?'

Touched by the simple truth of what Nam had said, the Sun took her into her palace and assigned her a storehouse by the fringe of her compound, in which she could live as she pleased. Nam eagerly took possession of the little shed and, expert as she was in housekeeping, quickly turned it into a clean and comfortable little dwelling, to the great delight of her benefactress, who then allowed her to work in her house as a servant.

For a time Nam lived a quiet, uneventful life. As may be supposed, she was sufficiently happy, and living inside the Sun's palace, she felt safe even from the threat of Hynroh. In fact, she was beginning to forget Hynroh altogether; she moved about freely and when alone in the shed, removed her odious and burdensome toad skin. Very soon, she grew bolder and would venture out to a nearby spring to bathe without her ugly mask.

But unfortunately—or fortunately—for her, one morning,

as she was on her way to the spring, she was secretly observed by the only child of the Sun, U Lur Mangkara, a dashing young prince, the darling of the blue realm, who had been out riding earlier than usual.

The prince was thunderstruck. He had never seen a creature of such exquisite beauty anywhere before. Seeing her as she really was, he ceased to wonder why she was called Nam, or Glory. To his mind she was the most glorious woman...but what was he saying? She was no woman, she was a divine fairy, a goddess in her own right. With his heart beating against his breast, the prince hurried home to his mother and told her all that he had discovered, excitedly pleading all the while to let him marry the strange maiden who had been hiding her loveliness under a loathsome camouflage. The Sun was equally amazed, but advised patience to her son, vowing that she would look into the matter herself and find out the terrible reasons that had compelled the fair one to live in the guise of a toad.

The very next day the Sun set about watching Nam's movements very carefully and soon discovered for herself what her son had told her. She resolved to destroy the toad skin once and for all, and make Nam her daughter-in-law. Having been a witness to Nam's modest and sweet nature, and then to her great beauty, she could have wished for no other woman to marry her son. Consequently, one morning while Nam was bathing at the spring, the Sun took away the toad skin, burnt it and replaced it with royal robes and all sorts of precious ornaments.

But Nam was far from pleased. She wept bitterly, complaining to the Sun that she was now in grave danger. She then recounted the whole story of her life, leading to her flight into that world in deep space. She told the Sun of the Tiger and his evil scheme to feast on her. She told her of Hynroh and how the Great Toad had condemned her to the

life of a toad by threatening to devour her if she ever
removed her skin. And now she was terrified of her, for her
dreaded influence was known to extend throughout heaven
and earth.

But the Sun, ruler of the universe, calmed her fears,
saying that she would never allow anyone to harm her future
daughter-in-law. At the mention of the word 'daughter-in-
law', Nam suddenly lost her fears and was at the same time
covered in confusion. Since the time she had set eyes on the
prince, she had harboured a secret love for him, but had
never dared hope, even in her wildest dreams, that he would
one day be her beloved husband. She lowered her head to
hide the happiness that suffused her at that moment. Seeing
her agitation, the Sun ruffled her long, dark hair and said
reassuringly, 'Yes, dear, I intend to compensate for the toad
skin with my very own son. And of course, that is also my
son's wish. He loves you with his very soul.'

Shortly after that announcement, Nam found herself the
happy bride of a very charming prince, at a wedding that was
participated in and witnessed by the crowns and coronets of
the whole universe. As a special gift to the bride, the Sun
blessed her with immortality, thus making her an equal
partner to her son.

Meanwhile, Hynroh, on learning that the Sun had
deliberately destroyed the toad skin and turned Nam into a
princess, was so enraged that she flew up into the sky and
tried to swallow up the Sun in one gulp. The Sun, an equally
powerful being, strove to ward off her onslaught, and a fierce
combat ensued, which was watched by mankind with bated
breath.

For a while the battle remained undecided. Slowly,
however, Hynroh began to gain the upper hand. But just
when the Sun was about to be devoured, the people on
Earth, who were worried for their life-giver, raised a resounding

racket, crying at the tops of their voices, beating on iron utensils, drums and whatever else that would make a noise, in order to scare off Hynroh. Hynroh was no coward, but fortunately for the Sun and the people, the deafening din had a draining influence on her magic powers, so that she was forced to let go of the Sun and flee.

Unable to satisfy her revenge on the Sun, Hynroh turned to the Moon, the Sun's only brother, who was living alone, and tried to eat him up instead. Unfortunately for her, here too she encountered the same problem with the people's clamour forcing her to leave the Moon alone and return to her jungle on earth.

To this day, however, Hynroh has neither forgiven the Sun nor forgotten her unsated thirst for vengeance. She is therefore seen making periodical attacks on both the Sun and her brother, in the hope that one day the people would be too preoccupied with their day-to-day living to notice what she was about.

---

[1]See 'The Seven Clans'.

The Sun and the Moon

$\mathcal{M}$y readers already know that Ramew, or Mother Earth, was the first of God's creations, and that her husband was Basa, who later came to be identified with the patron god of villages. They had five children of great powers and accomplishments. Among these five children were Ramew's first daughter, the Sun, and her only boy-child, the Moon. Because of the nature of the work entrusted to them when they grew up, they were sent by Ramew, in consultation with God, to the heavens, far away from their Earth-bound sisters, Water, Wind and Fire.

Alone in the sky, the two built a palace where they lived happily together, each loving and respecting the other as befitted a good brother and sister. The two never had any misunderstandings and shared their work willingly. Unfortunately, this quiet, idyllic routine was not fated to last for ever. The Sun and the Moon had been living alone for too long in the same house, and soon the Moon developed strange yearnings and passions for his own sister, a lovely woman whom the whole universe acknowledged as the most beautiful and glorious in all creation.

To be fair to the Moon, though, these yearnings did not sprout of their own, for they were encouraged to grow in his heart by the influence of spring, a season 'presided over by the spirit of mischief and madness', the madness of love, that is, which rose from the Earth to consume even a celestial being in the sky. But his sister was such a virtuous soul and had such a sense of propriety, such purity of thought, that it was quite impossible for him to approach her with such insanity. Indeed, a mere glance at her shining face and brilliant eyes, which seemed to look at him with the light of God Himself, was enough to discourage him from his impure thoughts. For some time, then, he suppressed his incestuous passions, considered by all to be among the most evil of desires.

One day during the fifth moon, however, while he was out observing the effect of the spring showers on the teeming life of Nature, he noticed the bees flitting from flower to flower as if they were testing the sweetness of each blossom's nectar of love. He heard birds in blooming copses singing love songs and cooing to each other. He saw little animals frisking about and fondling each other, and marked that even fierce brutes called each to each softly and made love. The sight of all these creatures mating so fired his heart and overwhelmed him with lust that he became quite crazed. Now truly possessed, he hurried his flight to where his sister was, shut the inner eye of his soul tightly, protested his love for her, and in the same breath asked for her hand in marriage.

At first the Sun thought she had heard her brother wrong, but when she realized that he was in earnest and that he did not see her as his sister any more, she blazed out in fury and said, 'You shameless creature! How dare you address such dirty words to me, your elder sister, who has bathed, cuddled and taken care of you like a mother? Get out of my house immediately! I would rather live alone than with a brother who is worse than the lowliest criminal!'

Banishing the Moon from her house, however, did not appease the anger of the Sun. She wanted to lay a curse on this brother who had degraded himself to the status of a beast. She wished to put a mark on him so that all heaven and earth should know his evil deed and avoid him for ever. Before he fled her house, therefore, she scooped up a basketful of ash from the hearth and emptied the whole of it over him so that he was covered from head to foot with it, and is so to this day.

Sobered and shamed beyond measure by the words and terrible rage of his sister, the Moon hastily departed from there to hide himself from her in the darkest part of the universe. And as he did not want ever to run into his sister again, he began from then on to venture out only at night. That is why today we see the Moon shining in the darkness of the night with a pale and hazy light, the result of the ash flung at him by the Sun.

Ren and the River Nymph

*M*any, many years ago, when Man and beast spoke the same language, and God and the fairies still frequented the human world, there lived a handsome fisherman known simply as Ren. His home was in the small village of Nongjri, some precipitous kilometres to the east of the ancient town of Sohra, or Cherrapunjee, as it is known to the outside world.

Ren lived with his old mother, who depended on him for everything. He rose before dawn and worked very hard all day, catching fish in the nearby river and selling his catch in the evening in the border markets called *haats*.

This daily grind kept Ren out of mischief but also made his life a very solitary one indeed. Everybody liked him, but he was too busy trying to feed his mother and himself to spend time with the village youths. And although he was the dream of every village girl, he never felt inclined to accompany his friends on their nightly trips to the dwellings of these lovely maidens, to court them with stories, songs and poetry, as was the practice. Too tired after a hard day's work, Ren usually stayed home at night, playing beautiful music on his two-stringed *duitara*. He slept the sound and peaceful sleep of one whose mind and heart were untouched by pain or longing.

But when Ren went fishing, it was almost always with friends. His favourite spot was the biggest pool in the river. It was almost as large as a small lake and very, very deep. The curious thing about these fishing trips was that Ren never went home empty-handed. While his friends often sat there all day without attracting a nibble, Ren's cane rope always had at least a dozen fishes dangling from it. His strange gift became the talk of the village. His friends joked that some good fairy had taken a liking to him and blessed him with his extraordinary good luck. His friends wished Ren further good fortune and said they were off to find another spot, so he could be alone with his fairy. From that day on, Ren fished at the pool alone.

One day, soon after his friends were gone, at the hour exactly between day and night, there rose from the glittering pool the river nymph herself. There she stood in her shimmering glory, smiling at the terrified Ren. But she spoke with such sweetness, that his fear vanished, and like any normal young man, he became spellbound by her beauty. He was sure she was a puriblei, a divine fairy, for the elders had told him that evil could not show so lovely a face.

There he stood, marvelling at the strange vision even as she introduced herself: 'I am Queen of the River Spirits, mistress of these waters. But it is not as a Queen that I have come.'

She was tall. The lines of her face were delicate. Her glossy black hair flowed down to her ankles. She was as beautiful as no other woman he had seen before. She wore a strange white robe of pure white silk. Instead of a *jaiñsem*,[1] she wore a belt studded with diamonds and gems of all shapes and colours. Her only other ornaments were her ruby earrings, and a golden signet ring. She did not even have a crown on her head, for, as she had said, she had come not as a queen.

Ren saw all this as if in a trance, for he was aware of nothing but her singular beauty, which smote him on the spot. Indeed, he could not help falling head over heels in love with her, especially when she encouraged that feeling herself, with eyes that beckoned him and shone like sunbeams. However, Ren revived soon after and, remembering his manners, introduced himself and eagerly engaged her in conversation.

As it always is with people in love, very soon, the two of them began talking to each other in the most secret and intimate terms. The fairy queen confided: 'Yes, it was I who wooed you with fish by the dozens every day, just as your friends said, although they had spoken in jest.'

'But how could you, a Goddess, court a simple fisherman like me?' Ren reacted in excited disbelief.

'It is not important to me what you do for a living,' the river nymph replied. 'It is how you conduct yourself in life...it was your manliness and purity of heart that first drew me to you.'

Now certain that she was in earnest, Ren on his part vowed never to betray her in any way. The pledges done, the lovers parted, promising they would meet again the next day—same place, same time.

That evening, Ren couldn't stop smiling to himself. So much so, that his mother wondered what was wrong with him. In love for the first time, he ate mechanically and found himself waiting impatiently for the hour when he would meet his beloved. Noon finally came. The fairy queen appeared. They spent the day in much the same way: declaring their love, as lovers never seem to tire of doing.

Their secret meetings carried on until they could stand to be separated no longer. Neither was satisfied with just a few hours of each other's company each day. They wanted to be together always, forever. But there was a problem. Ren could not leave his old mother. Nor could he follow his nymph into the water's magic depths. In spite of her assurances to the contrary, he could not help but find the prospect of living below the surface of the earth, under all that body of water, intimidating. As she could as easily live on both dry land and underwater, he asked her to leave her enchanted world and stay with him in the land of humans. Not wanting to displease him in any way, the fairy queen agreed to follow Ren to his house on one condition:

'The hut must be spotlessly clean, for we cannot live in filth. The broom with which you sweep that dirt must nowhere be in sight,' she said.

Ren readily agreed to her condition. He thought they were quite reasonable. They set a date, and Ren hurried home to tell his mother that he would soon be bringing home his new bride, the river nymph.

Anything could happen in those days, anything could be expected. God and Man were close, the spirits wandered the land and it was said that they did their buying and selling in the very same markets that humans did. So Ren's mother wasn't a bit surprised by the news. Instead, she was more excited than she had ever been in her entire life: 'A daughter from the Gods!' she exclaimed. 'Rest assured, my son, that the hut will be clean. Don't worry your head about it. Your mother will make it shine like the sun.' And she scrubbed and she cleaned as she prepared to welcome her extraordinary daughter-in-law.

When the day arrived, Ren took the fairy queen to his home. As was the custom, he announced her arrival from the doorway. His mother, who had been watching from the window, hurried to the door. She embraced the exquisite nymph, caressed her soot-black hair and finally asked her to relax and make herself at home on a low cane stool specially ordered for the occasion.

The fairy queen too was very happy to have a kind, affectionate mother-in-law welcoming her home like that. Before she sat down, she looked around the room. She was curious to see what her future home was like. Suddenly, she froze. Her face darkened as her look of happiness changed to one of utter pain. Mother and son looked in the direction of her gaze. Alas! Everything was undone! Ren's mother, old and absent-minded, or perhaps too excited, after all the washing, dusting and sweeping, had left, the broom in its usual place in a corner behind the door. She had quite forgotten that it was to be nowhere near the house.

Sobbing, she turned to her daughter-in-law to beg her forgiveness. But the gentle spirit had fallen in a faint: so overcome was she at the sight of the inauspicious broom. Ren, weeping bitterly himself, carried her outside. In a while she revived, and joined the mother and son in their tears. She felt she was to blame for it all. She asked them to forgive her. Then she fled back to her pool.

For the first time in human history the broom had become a symbol of a broken promise.

Ren knew that it was now his turn to choose. This would be a painful choice. He gazed at his mother whom he loved with all his heart, and against whom he bore no malice. She was old and feeble.... Then he shifted his gaze towards the pool where his love was waiting.... He felt as if his heart was being torn asunder by the conflicting emotions. What was he to do? Whom was he to satisfy?

Seeing Ren's suffering, his mother selflessly urged him to think only of his own happiness. 'After all,' she said, 'I have not many days to live. Besides, it is not our custom for a son to bring his wife to his mother's home. Go to her, my son, God wills it so.' With such words, and many others that showed how unbounded and ungrudging her love for her son was, the old woman finally persuaded Ren to leave his home and follow his wife.

Ren embraced his mother for the last time, showered her with kisses from head to foot and handed her a little bagful of precious stones, gifted to him that very day by his nymph, so as to enable her to live in reasonable comfort for the remaining years of her life. Besides this material provision, Ren also offered his mother one consolation: 'Mother,' he said, as he looked at her one last time, 'listen to the river. As long as it roars, you will know that I live....'

With these words, Ren left to join his fairy queen in the enchanted watery depths of the river, which became known from that time as River Ren. Alone in the world, his mother sought comfort in listening to the peculiar roaring sound the river suddenly began to emit each morning, the sound which she had come to identify with her son continuing existence. Every time she heard the sound, she knew her son was near. But she was old, and she died soon after. Now nobody cares about the sound of Ren's life.

From the story, the Khasis learnt the secret of driving away spirits with the broom—a ritual which is practised even today.

---

[1]Khasi outer garment comprising two long cloths of cotton, silk, etc., draped over the shoulders.

The Man-eating Serpent, U Thlen

The legend of U Thlen, swallower of humans, is a living one, and to this day people talk about this man-eating, blood-sucking serpent as they would talk of the plague, cancer, tuberculosis or any other killer disease, for that is what this monster represents now: the cause of a deadly illness where a person loses his natural colour, and grows thin and weak, with his face and belly bloated. They say the keepers of this creature, and the killers in their employment, whose business it is to hunt men for their blood, are still very active in some parts of the Khasi Hills.

At first, Thlen did not need a keeper or a hunter to feed him with the blood of humans. But the story of how he became transformed from a maneater to a drinker of blood, and how he metamorphosed into a dependent creature, really began somewhere in the dim past, where Man and the spirits were said to have rubbed shoulders.

According to the legend, Thlen was an evil creature with supernatural powers, living in the wilderness of Sohra. This was, of course, during ancient times. In those days it was said that he could change his shape and size at will, but his favourite form was that of a gigantic python, lying with his gargantuan mouth open in a cave at Daiñthlen, a place in the western suburb of Sohra, and his tail tapering off towards Ïingkhrong, some kilometres away in Sohra proper. But how did Thlen come to live in that tunnel? Where did he come from?

Thlen's origin is traced to dubious, though superhuman parentage. He was the son of Ka Kma Kharai, depraved daughter of U Mawlong Syliem, the chief god of the area around Mawsmai, a village to the south of Sohra. Ka Kma Kharai herself was a deity presiding over caves and trenches, but her name was associated among the gods with profligate living, and she was shunned by all but the most inferior and malicious in their world. Having lived the life of a harlot and degenerated into an evil fairy, Ka Kma Kharai was eventually cursed with a bastard, a deformed demon whose birth so roused the wrath of her father that she had to flee her home and look for new haunting grounds. By and by she came towards the northern territory of Sohra, and there she decided to make its beautiful gorges her permanent home. But, a harlot by nature, she soon found her child a burden and decided to tuck him away in a cave at the foot of the Pomdoloi Falls.

The cave was chosen by her for a reason. Being a malignant spirit, an enemy to mankind, she was determined that her son should grow up on nothing but human flesh. She had, therefore, specially chosen this cave as it was en route to Rangjyrteh, a large town to the west of Sohra, with the biggest and most popular marketplace in Ri Hynñiew Trep[1] in those days, and hence with many wayfarers passing to and from it. And so it came to pass that since the day he was installed in the cave, Thlen lay in wait for passers-by, and whenever people went through it in groups of three, five or seven, he would suck in the straggler and swallow him whole. And that was also how he earned his name, by the manner of his consumption of humans: leaving no trace of even a full-grown man in a matter of minutes.

The first man to vanish was a marketer from Sylhet, or a Shilotia, as the Khasis described him. All the marketers of the area, from Rangjyrteh to Sylhet, organized a big search party around the Pomdoloi Falls. The search party continued for many weeks, but instead of finding the man, or at least recovering his body for the last rites, more and more men were reported missing from the search party itself. This so alarmed the people that they gave up the search and went to the augurs to seek from God the reason for this strange and evil phenomenon.

God, who saw everything and who perfectly understood that Thlen's design was to wipe out the human race from these beautiful hills, directed the augurs through signs and symbols to seek the help of U Syiem Syrmoh in the avatar of Suitnoh. Suitnoh had many other manifestations as well. Throughout the length and breadth of Ri Hynñiew Trep, he was worshipped as U Syiem Kyrsan, the chief of all the guardian spirits whose duty was to restore health and virtue to the world. He was seen, too, in the form of U Ryngkew-U-Basa, the patron god of villages. His favourite haunt was believed to be the sacred grove of Laitryngew, to the area north of Sohra known as Ka Law Suitnoh, whose fame as a holy place was such that even the Dkhars[2] from the plains of

Surma used to come and perform their many religious rites there. This powerful god was invoked with many offerings and sacrifices, each of which was meant to paint the cruelty of Thlen, the misery of mankind, and, most of all, to place before Suitnoh Man's ardent plea for help in ending the malevolent creature's savage slaughter of humankind. As the restorer of good health in the world, Suitnoh could not ignore the plea or tolerate Thlen's monstrous deeds. He could not stand by and watch unconcerned while this fiend was devouring the human race one by one. He readily gave his word that he would come to the rescue of mankind.

Having committed himself to the task, Suitnoh made his first stop at the house of the *Lyngdoh*, or chief priest, of Law Suitnoh. Appearing to the man in human form, he commanded the Lyngdoh to build a smithy some distance from the cave of Thlen, and there to make a huge iron ball and a pair of giant tongs. When this was done and the implements prepared, Suitnoh waited for the next market day at Iew Bah Sohra, approached Thlen and greeted him like a long-lost friend. There was nothing unusual about this, for the two knew each other well, both being from the spirit world.

'How are you, *Um*?'[3] Suitnoh called out to Thlen. 'It's been a long time since we met.'

'I know, Um, I know,' returned Thlen from his hole. 'It's been ages, in fact, since I last set eyes on you.'

'I'm on my way to the market of the gods at Iew Bah Sohra. Would you care for anything to eat, Um?' Suitnoh offered.

I wouldn't mind, Um, I wouldn't mind at all,' said Thlen. 'Only, make sure you bring me a piece of that famous Sohra pork, I have grown a little sick of human flesh lately.'

After this brief exchange, Suitnoh took his leave of Thlen and went away to the smithy, happy that his plans were going smoothly. At the smithy he ordered that the iron ball be heated to the highest degree.

Come evening, when the iron ball had turned white hot, Suitnoh went back to Thlen's cave, carrying the ball of iron between the giant tongs, and said, 'Ahoi, Um! I have brought you the pork. Open up, Um, open your mouth, it's a rather large piece.'

Thlen, who had grown enormously fat from eating so much human flesh, had become rather sluggish and did not stir from his cave. Neither did he have reason to suspect that anything was amiss. Thanking Suitnoh for keeping his promise, he opened his mouth to swallow the pork at one gulp. But Suitnoh was not satisfied. He said, 'Open up some more, Um, open up some more. It's larger than you think.'

Thlen opened his jaws wide, till they quite shut out his eyes. And that was the moment Suitnoh was waiting for. With a powerful thrust, he shoved the burning-hot iron ball down Thlen's throat and immediately vanished from the spot. The ball burnt up Thlen's insides, causing him such agony that he began to writhe and squirm, toss from side to side, and thrash about with such violence that his movements caused an earthquake all over Sohra and the surrounding country.

It was also said that his death throes were so powerful that they made deep cracks in the land and created one of the most famous gorges in Sohra. This later came to be called Ka Riat Mawïew. The hour of his death proved traumatic for the people in the area. The earth shook, hills came tumbling down, houses and all, and the air was filled with so much debris that the sun was completely blotted out. Fortunately for the people, the quake did not last for long, for Thlen died soon after the iron had burnt through his vital parts.

With the death of Thlen, Suitnoh directed the Lyngdoh to call all the people of Ri Hynñiew Trep and also all those

people in the plains of Sylhet whose kith and kin had died
in the jaws of the monster, to gather by the river near
Thlen's cave the following day. Thus, felt Suitnoh, they
could all share in a feast on the monster's flesh, and consume
it all. Suitnoh was emphatic that all of Thlen's flesh be
eaten, all in one day and at the exact place where he had
been killed. Not even a tiny bit of the flesh, he said, should
be taken anywhere else or left for another day. However, he
offered no explanation for his strange instruction other than
that it should be obeyed if everyone really wanted to be rid
of the evil creature forever.

The people obeyed his call; came from here, there and
everywhere. They converged upon the sinister cave, hauled
Thlen's body from his lair and cut it into pieces, cooking the
portions in large cauldrons and burning to a cinder the rest
of the skin, bones and every other part that was not edible.
All this done, they then celebrated their triumph on a grand
scale, pouring out a free libation of rice beer for everyone, to
give their appetite a fine edge, and kill whatever reluctance
there was in the way of making a hearty meal of Thlen. Their
appetite thus roused, one and all, young and old, ate to their
hearts' content, leaving not a morsel anywhere.

After the feast, the gathering broke up and all went their
separate ways, except for the local elders who stayed behind
to complete the ritual of the feast and pay obeisance to God,
the Keeper, the Creator. These elders also carved out on the
rocks the figure of Thlen, the serpent, and all the cooking
articles used in the feast to enable future generations to learn
the story of the demonic creature. Before leaving the place,
they also renamed Pomdoloi Falls as Kshaid Daiñthlen or
Daiñthlen Falls, meaning the place where Thlen was killed
and carved up.

But, unknown among the revellers, there was an old
woman who had kept back a bite of that serpent flesh for her

only son, who could not attend the feast. At home she put the meat in a basket where she kept dried fish, with the intention of feeding her son as soon as he returned home. But, as if confounded by some mysterious power, the woman kept forgetting what she'd done, until one day, when she was alone, the piece of flesh called out to her and said, 'Old woman, keep me and I will make you rich. I have in me the power to give you all the gold and silver in the world. Keep me and I will make you prosper in everything that you do.'

The old woman turned towards the basket and saw a small snake looking at her and talking to her as if it were another human being. She suddenly remembered the piece of flesh and understood what was happening. Thlen had resurrected himself from the piece of dead meat. That was why Suitnoh had been so particular that the last of the creature's flesh be consumed—he had known what otherwise could happen.

But now Thlen was in the old woman's house. Realizing this, she was gripped by a feeling of great dread and would have rushed out of the house had Thlen not spoken again.

'I have promised you riches, old woman, but think carefully what will happen to you if you inform on me. You are as much an enemy to mankind as I am, for you have given me back my life.'

That stopped the woman. She knew only too well what would happen to her if the people discovered her error. She would be stoned to death. On the other hand, if she kept Thlen a secret, there were all those riches. The thought of wealth further tilted her mind in favour of preserving this demon, and that was exactly what she did.

Thlen, too, made her wealthy and prosperous, according to his promise. But one day, when he thought she was finally won over by her ill-gotten fortune, he called out to her again, and said, 'Old woman, look, I have made you prosperous and

given you whatever you wanted. Now return my favour.
Bring me a *lang-thoh-khlieh*,[4] a goat with a spotted head, so I
can eat too.'

The old woman brought him a goat with markings on its
head. But instead of being pleased, Thlen was angry. 'I asked
you to bring me a goat with a spotted head. What animal is
this that you have brought!' he bellowed. 'Bring me someone
like you.' When the old woman understood that by lang-thoh-
khlieh, he was euphemistically referring to humans to eat,
she trembled from head to foot and replied, 'Forgive me, my
lord, but from where will I get humans for you to eat? They
surely won't come by themselves!'

'That is your business,' replied Thlen sternly. 'But if you
don't do as I say, I shall begin feasting on your family.'

And true to his word, in a couple of days, the old woman
found one of her grandsons dead, for no apparent reason.
Now thoroughly frightened, the woman began to look around
for desperate men who would kill for money and bring back
the blood of the victim to her, so that she could feed it to
her serpent. And the job was not an easy one since Thlen
refused to accept anything else but Khasi blood, saying, 'They
tried to destroy me. It is no longer a simple matter of feeding
on humans. My thirst is for Khasi blood alone.'

It was from that time that the practice of hiring paid
killers, or *nongshohnoh*, for Thlen developed. The old woman
used a special brew of rice beer called *kyiad tangsnem* to spur
on the killers and to render them ruthless and completely
devoid of conscience, so that a human life would seem no
more to them than a flitting butterfly. In this way the old
woman and her children propagated the practice of keeping
Thlen for riches, till it grew into a very popular evil practice
in some parts of Ri Khasi, notably Ri Sohra.

Today it is said that Thlen punishes the keepers who
cannot keep him fed, not only by killing one or two of their

children, but also by shaming them before the world by climbing on to rooftops and assuming the form of a cat, a smelt, or several other animal forms. The keepers on their part would try to keep him happy by offering sacrifices in the form of blood—or when blood was hard to come by, in the form of hair and a piece of cloth cut from unsuspecting victims. This hair or piece of cloth would then be converted by Thlen himself into the image of a particular victim, which would be made to dance on a silver plate to the eerie throbbing of a small drum at midnight. At the end of this evil ritual, the serpent would feast a little at a time on the image, starting from the feet upwards. This midnight ritual would continue for some time and when nothing of the image was left, the real victim, who would have been suffering at home all the agonies simulated on his image all the while, would eventually die.

But Thlen is supposed to be powerless against those from the Syiem clan, because Suitnoh, his destroyer, was himself a syiem, or king, a ruler among gods, servants of the one God.

---

[1]Khasi and Jaiñtia Hills.

[2]A person from the plains of mainland India or Bangladesh is referred to as a Dkhar by Khasis.

[3]Um: literally, brother-in-law, here an endearing term.

[4]The Khasi word lang-thoh-khlieh literally means a goat with a spotted head. The legend does not explain why a human is referred to as such by Thlen. It could only be a euphemism or some mystifying metaphor.

The Legend of Ka Pahsyntiew

*I*n ancient times it was said that spirits haunted the forests on the hills around what we now call Lum Shyllong or Shyllong Peak. The chief of these spirits dwelled on the highest and most thickly wooded hill. In those times, the people of the villages surrounding the hills did not know much about rites and rituals. It was enough for them to pray to God, U Blei, morning, and night. Although they knew about the hill spirits and were afraid to go anywhere near them, they did not think it necessary to make offerings to them. It was not till a village elder, a man of great wisdom and understanding of the mysteries of life, had started making sacrifices to the chief of the spirits, that the villagers learnt about propitiating and paying obeisance to more than the one supreme God that they knew.

The elder had learnt the rites from the people of Sohra, who worshipped God, U Blei, through the mediation of certain gods and goddesses. He had seen how the people prayed to U Mawlong Syiem, the chief of the spirit world in the countryside around Sohra. He had watched the religious ceremonies performed for U Suitnoh, the god of health, who lived in the sacred forest of Law Suitnoh at Laitryngew, so that he might look after the well-being of the people.

The elder wanted his village to have its own guardian god. So he taught his people how to pray to the chief spirit of the hills, whom he called Shulong or the Self-Begotten. From that time on the chief spirit became known as U Lei Shulong, or U Lei Shyllong as he is known today. By and by, U Lei Shyllong became the patron god of the villages situated around Lum Shyllong, and everyone throughout the length and breadth of Ri Hynñiew Trep, the land of the Khasis, began to pray to him.

This pleased U Lei Shyllong very much. He sent for his daughter and directed her to go and live among his human subjects. The goddess turned herself into a beautiful maiden and went to live in a cave called Krem Marai, near the village of Pomlakrai on the peak called Lum Shyllong. It was a lonely spot. Only a few boys and girls went there once in a while, to graze their cattle and goats nearby. But it didn't take the exploring children long to discover the lovely lady sitting in the sun by the entrance to her cave. This strange and beautiful woman, sitting all alone in the middle of nowhere, struck terror in their hearts and they fled the scene to report the matter to their parents and elders.

Soon, word of the mysterious woman at Krem Marai spread like wildfire to the four corners of Ri Hynñiewtrep.

The people, who were quite superstitious in those days, began to avoid the place for fear of the strange woman whom they thought was some kind of spirit.

One man among them, however, was not afraid. His name was Sati Mylliemngap, an elder from the village of Nongkseh, respected for his wisdom and insight. The rumour about a beautiful woman alone in a cave in the wilderness inspired his adventurous spirit and he resolved, come what may, to pay her a visit one day.

Sati set out for the cave on a splendid spring morning. Along the way, birds sang their love songs; wildflowers, nameless, rainbow-hued, danced in the breeze; the scented air seemed to urge him on, as if to a predestined rendezvous.

Near the cave, he picked his way carefully through the undergrowth. Every now and then he stopped to look for the maiden. Suddenly, there she was, sunning herself at the cave's entrance—just as the children had described. She had a little orchid in her hand, a *Lamat Ïong*, the black-eyed bloom.

Sati's jaw dropped as he gazed in wonder at her strange loveliness. Her skin was fair, and as smooth as spring water. Her eyes were blue as the clear sky. Her long, flowing, dark hair cascaded down her back. She was not dressed like a Khasi girl. Her robe was a creamy yellow, of a cloth quite different from silk spun by the villagers. She wore no *jaiñsem*,[1] which was quite unheard of for a local girl. As Sati stared at her, she caught sight of him and, with a little cry, disappeared inside the cave, which even bold Sati could not bring himself to enter.

But that was not the end of it. Sati stayed where he was, calling out to her: 'Dear Kong,'[2] he said. 'Why do you run from me... Don't be afraid... I mean you no harm.'

When she did not come, he pleaded and coaxed her with gentle words of endearment: 'I'm an old man with neither strength nor inclination to harm you. I'm old enough to be your father; come talk to me...all I want is to help you.'

Nothing worked however, and exhausted, he sat down for a while, to think. It wasn't long before an idea struck him. He had noticed some wild flowers blooming some distance away. Since the maiden seemed to be quite fond of flowers, he quickly went off to pick and fashion some into a bouquet, which he laid before the cave entrance. Then he called aloud:

'I give up. I'll leave now and not pester you again. But before I go, here are some flowers as a token of my goodwill. Please accept them. I'll put them here and go.'

That was exactly what he did. But having gone a little way, he doubled back by another path. He hid quietly by the side of the cave and waited. After a while, the shy maiden peeped out. She looked around to make sure the coast was clear, and stooped to pick up the bouquet.

This was just what Sati had been waiting for. He ran up to her and overpowered her in one grasp, while all the time trying to calm her fears and crying, 'I mean you no harm... Don't be afraid... I just want know more about you...' After a while, the woman calmed down a little.

Sati begged her forgiveness for playing such a trick on her. Once more he told her that he did not mean to harm her, and that, to the contrary, he had only wanted to help her. He said the people in the villages had become very agitated and fearful on coming to know about her stay in the cave. It was only to prevent anything untoward from happening that he had come, at the request of the village council of elders, to find out more about her, and why and how she had come to dwell in those lonely backwoods.

Reassured by the gentle manner of her captor, and convinced that she was talking to a true representative of the village council, the goddess revealed everything to a very astonished and reverential Sati. She told him how her father, happy with the people's unbounded faith in him, had sent her to be the progenitress of the Syiem clan, which would later become the ruling clan of Hima Shyllong. For the time being, however, she urged Sati not to disclose anything of all this except to the council of elders, which must also be sworn to secrecy.

The now elated Sati paid his obeisance and, promising to do exactly as she had told him, took her home. At home the goddess caused quite a sensation. People, neighbours, friends and relatives flocked to Sati's house to catch a glimpse of the strange woman. Sati introduced her to them as his adopted daughter, Ka Pahsyntiew, 'the one lured by flowers'. He chose the name, as the goddess had not wished to reveal her real name to anyone.

Meanwhile, the elders of the council met, and having learnt everything about the goddess from Sati, resolved to get her married to the most eligible bachelor in the land: the bravest, the strongest, the wisest and the most handsome youth they could find. After a long, hard quest they finally chose a youth from the Ri War[3] village of Nongjri, a young man called Kongngor whom they brought to Nongkseh for the wedding—which was the biggest and most memorable event of those times.

The moon was new, the moon was full. Time flew by and life for the couple slipped from one happy year to another. Pahsyntiew gave birth to many charming sons and daughters who grew up to be strong, intelligent and noble-hearted. They were the pride of the land, loved and respected by all. Kongngor, who doted on his divinely exquisite wife and dedicated his entire life to the welfare of his family, thought their happiness could never end.

But then, one day, Pahsyntiew called her children to her. As they sat before her with their father she said, 'My dear

Kongngor, my children. For so long I have hidden my true self from you, thinking only of your happiness. Now the time has come when I must go back to my own world. I am the daughter of U Lei Shyllong, sent by my father to give the people their own rulers. And rulers are what my sons shall be. I have done my duty and must return. Your father is a capable man, my children. I leave you to him with my blessing...'

Kongngor and his children were heartbroken. There was much crying and questioning, but since it was decreed that Pahsyntiew should return to her own kind, there was nothing anybody could do about it. With a pained heart and tearful eyes Pahsyntiew blessed her children and left the house for her cave at Krem Marai and was never seen again.

Kongngor and his children grieved for her a long time. But with the love of the people they were able to overcome their sorrow. By and by, true to the words of Pahsyntiew, Kongngor's eldest son was made the syiem or king of a new state formed from the villages surrounding the peak of Shyllong, which later became Hima Shyllong or the State of Shyllong. The new syiem ruled his people well. With the help of his able brothers his state grew large and strong. In no time at all it became one of the most powerful states in the 'land of the thirty syiems and twelve dolois', which is another name for Ri Hynñiew Trep.

The people were greatly pleased with all this and together with their syiem they built the *iïngsad*, the ancestral house of the syiem's mother, Pahsyntiew, at Nongkseh. Here they performed all the ceremonies of the state. And here, in accordance with the customs of the land, lived the syiem's eldest sister, the syiemsad.

When their only other sister, the youngest of the family, grew up, she was married to a young man from Mylliem. For reasons not very clear to us today, soon after her sister's marriage, the syiemsad moved to Nongkrem, some kilometres away from Nongkseh, her original home. Following her relocation, the ïingsad of Hima Shyllong was also transferred to Nongkrem where it remains until today.

---

[1]Khasi outer garment comprising two long cloths of cotton, silk, etc., draped over the shoulders.

[2]Honorary Khasi title meaning Miss or Sister.

[3] Villages bordering present-day Bangladesh.

The Fight Between Kyllang and Symper

𝒰 Lum Kyllang, or the Kyllang Hill, is in Hima Nongkhlaw, in the West Khasi Hills on the left of the road from Khadsawphra village to Mawnai. This hill is composed of a large single dome-like rock and is surrounded by other, smaller hills, making it look like a sovereign amidst courtiers. U Lum Symper, or the Symper Hill, on the other hand, is to the east of village Kmawan in Hima Maharam, also in the West Khasi Hills. The hill stands alone and seems to rise from the flat ground like a giant mound of loam, deciduous trees and dark boulders, fashioned by some aboriginal titan.

The story goes that in the old days the two hills stood side by

side at Kmawan, instead of being as far away from each other
as they are now. They were said to be the dwelling places of
two powerful mountain spirit brothers, U Kyllang and U
Symper. Of the two brothers, Kyllang was the better known,
for, being a warlike and malignant spirit, he used to travel far
from home to plunder the land of U Lei Synteng, or the God
of Synteng, in present-day Jaiñtia Hills. When on these
forays, Kyllang almost always used his terrible weapon, a kind
of fierce cyclonic storm that uprooted trees and carried away
houses and everything else in its wake. Of Symper, nothing
much is known except that he was gentler in his ways,
though quite as potent as Kyllang.

For many years the two brothers lived happily next to
each other, although sometimes they used to have heated
altercations—as all brothers do. Such arguments especially
occurred when Kyllang was about to set off on one of his
incursions. As the elder brother, who had first seen the Sun
and the Moon, and was therefore, saner in his thoughts and
feelings, Symper did not approve of the violent ways of
Kyllang. Symper would always try to stop Kyllang from going
on such raids, saying, 'My dear brother, why do you have to
be so aggressive to others? Why do you terrorize those poor
humans in Ri Pnar?' What wrong have they done you?'

But Kyllang, who would be in a particularly belligerent
mood at such moments, would brook no interference from
anyone, and would retort, 'You are nothing but a weakling
and a spoilsport. Do you think those people would be grateful
to you for nagging me day and night and by always trying to
do good? Oh, no, they would only take you for a coward! You
asked me what wrong they have done me. Isn't the very fact
that they worship U Lei Synteng reason enough for you?'

According to Kyllang, humans needed to be reminded
now and then of the powers of true gods. 'Have we not
governed the earth since the beginning of time?' he would

demand. The humans, he would repeat, needed to be reminded who the real masters of the earth were, and his way, Kyllang maintained, was the best form of reminder.

These quarrels, however, never took on the dimensions of anything more serious than routine sibling rivalry and did not spoil the good brotherly relationship between the two gods. But one day, Kyllang, on being provoked by U Lei Synteng, went berserk and dealt out cruel penalties to the people of Ri Pnar and to anyone else who happened to cross his path. On this occasion, not only did he use his cyclonic storm but, for the first time, unleashed his toxic force, spreading measles, chickenpox and smallpox everywhere. Following this onslaught, there were cries of death and suffering throughout the land.

This so angered Symper that he hauled up his brother the moment he returned. 'Are you mad?' he raged at him. 'Are you a mountain spirit or a lowly demon to cause such slaughter and bring such frightful misery among the poor and hapless? If U Lei Synteng had offended you, why did you wreak such havoc on humans? Do you think that by beating his servants, an offending master would be taught a lesson? You are cruel, stupid and cowardly!'

Kyllang, whose thirst for vengeance had not been quenched, was enraged further by these insults. He slapped his senior in the face and snarled, 'Whom are you calling a lowly demon? Whom are you calling a coward?' Giving Symper a crushing kick, he warned, 'I'll teach you the lesson of your life! This time, I'll squash you like the insect that you are!

Now, to raise a finger against one's elder brother is bad enough, but to use one's foot against him is no less than an act of sacrilege. Symper's normally slow anger was now fully aroused, and in his wrath he retaliated with all his might.

A savage and tumultuous battle ensued that caused such

devastation in the surroundings that men fled their homes, and animals their haunts, to save their lives. As was his wont during a fight, Kyllang produced his frightful weapon, the cyclonic storm, and tried to overwhelm his brother with it. But bad luck was in store for Kyllang. As he raised his storm and looked for stones with which to fire a barrage at Symper, he found, to his chagrin, that there were no stones on the hill where he lived. In desperation he gouged out from the hill large chunks of earth and tried to smother Symper with them.

Symper, however, was strategically better placed, for where he lived the place was strewn with large boulders. Picking them up one by one, he let fly at Kyllang for the whole of that day, till towards evening Kyllang could bear the pain no more and fled the scene, rolling away with his home, the hill, towards Nongum near Khadsawphra, where he has remained to this day. And thus it came to pass that the two brothers separated forever.

Kyllang carried the marks of battle with him to the new home, and today his hill is seen in the form of a huge granite block, because he had scooped out all the covering soil from it during his fight with Symper. The hill of Symper, on the other hand, has now become a fertile place because of all the soil hurled on him by Kyllang.

---

[1]Present-day Jaiñtia Hills.

The Death of Lapalang, the Stag

The story of U Sier Lapalang, the stag, and how he came to be hunted down on the slopes of the Shyllong Peak, is not only a favourite amongst huntsmen, shepherds and cowherds, but is also a story that has moved the heart of all those mothers who have, at one time or the other, suffered the tragedy of losing their only child.

U Sier Lapalang was the only son of a doting mother, an old deer who lived a long time ago on the plains of Bangla, by the foothills of Ri Khasi, in the land where the sun burnt down through spring, summer, autumn and winter. The two of them led a quiet, happy life. The food was plentiful amidst the reeds and bulrushes of the many streams that flowed from the hills and nothing was wanting.

And certainly not by way of motherly care and affection, for the old deer loved her son as only a kind mother, without anyone else in her life, could. In fact, she doted on him and worshipped him; observing him from head to foot and seeing the magnificence of his antlers, the power of his muscles and the swiftness of his feet, she was sure there was not another creature on earth more beautiful than her son. Loving him to the point of distraction, the indulgent mother never did anything to thwart him in any way, but always sought more ways to make his life happy.

Basking in the glory of his mother's unqualified love, the young stag became a victim of her unceasing shower of flattery, and soon grew vain and arrogant. By and by, contrary to his mother's expectation, he found his life to be too dull and uneventful. He was sick of the flat land, its heat and the uninterrupted monotony. He was sick of having only reeds and bulrushes for food, and most of all he was sick of the confines of home and longed to escape to the distant hills that rose above the plains and seemed to touch the blue realm itself.

Many a time he had listened to his old mother recounting tales about the hills: about how beautiful and cool they were; and the variety of rich delicacies that could be found there. And many a time his interest was aroused by his mother's report of the plentiful growth there of his favourite food, the nicely bitter plant called *jangew*, which grew only scantily in the foothills. A strong, active youth, his heart burnt with restless energy, and one spring day he gave his mother the shock of her life by announcing his intention to venture into the beckoning highlands.

With tears in her eyes, the old mother tried to talk him out of his foolhardy plan and said, 'Yes, my darling son, I have told you that yonder is the land of the gods. It is a paradise blessed with cool forests, green hill slopes and beautiful valleys through which run laughing streams and streamlets, the life-givers of your favourite fare, jangew, and the flowers whose scent during spring spreads out to the very fields of Surma. But listen, my dear, yonder is also a land of fierce warriors who will brook no intrusion into their territories. Surely, they will make fine sport of you! Consider awhile, my dearest love, before you rush into such a place. Think of your old mother pining away alone...please, my love, do not go.'

So saying, she clung to his neck as if determined to detain him by force. But the young stag shook her off and said, 'Don't be foolish, my mother. Why are you afraid? Am I not, in your own description, one of the most accomplished creatures on earth? I am young, I am strong, I am swift. I can easily fight my way through the warriors and outrun their murderous arrows if the Khasis dare obstruct me in my path. Rest assured, my mother, nothing will happen to me. And besides, I won't be away for long.'

However, the mother was far from being reassured and she wept bitterly as she watched her only son scale the hills and approach the land which was fraught with so many dangers.

But for U Sier Lapalang, the thought of danger had never been as far away from his mind as it was at that time. Oblivious of everything else but the beauty of the surroundings and the pleasantness of the cool heights, he went further and further into the strange country, following the trail of jangew.

Days became weeks, weeks became months, but the jangew-besotted youth never once thought of home and his mother. On and on he went, until one day, he stood in all his glory on the slope of Shyllong Peak, in the very heart of Ri Khasi. Here, his favourite food was so in plenty and the climate of spring so congenial that he dallied much longer than he had done in the other places, from Sohra upwards. And this lingering proved to be his undoing, for as he was revelling in the sheer joy of the moment, frolicking about, he was suddenly spotted by cowherds grazing their cattle nearby. The unexpected sight of a stag so roused their excitement that they immediately left their herds and gave the alarm, shouting, 'A stag! A stag! There's a stag nearby!'

Soon, this shout was taken up by fieldworkers, who abandoned their work and joined in the chase. The din raised by the cowherds and farmers attracted the attention of others, who came from here, there and everywhere, armed with bows and arrows and anything they could get hold of on the spur of the moment. Now, the hunt began in earnest.

Scared out of his wits, U Sier Lapalang fled from hill to hill, trying his best to elude his pursuers. But his best was just not good enough, for though he was indeed young and strong and swift and easily outran one set of hunters, another set, with their baying dogs, would converge upon him from another direction, making his speed useless and his flight hopeless. At last, after his mad rush from hill to hill, U Sier Lapalang began to tire, and tiring, he stopped, desperately looking about for a hiding place. It was then that an arrow with a long spearhead struck his chest and pierced his heart. U Sier Lapalang looked at it in stupefaction and fell down, dead even before he hit the ground. At this sight, a thunderous roar of triumph erupted as the hunters fell upon his body, tied his four feet together and bore him homewards on a long pole, with much chanting and rejoicing.

Meanwhile, the old mother, who had been deserted in the plains, became quite ill with worry as her son failed to return, even after such a long, long time had elapsed. She could not eat, she could not sleep, but pined away for her son day and night, until at last, unable to bear the suspense any longer, she left her home to look for him in the land of her enemies. In the hills she roamed about from place to place for many days, without seeing either hide or hair of her son. One day, however, as she was walking listlessly about, she suddenly heard a great noise, as of people celebrating. She stopped dead in her tracks, to ascertain what she had heard, and sure enough, it was a procession of laughing, cheering and loudly chanting people, who were all the while dancing round the body of something which dangled from a long pole.

She was about to flee when she recognized, with sudden anguish, that the body was none other than that of her slain son, U Sier Lapalang. Realizing this, she lost all her fear of Man and his arrows and rushed headlong to the scene, crying loud lamentations in such a plaintive and mournful voice and in a language so steeped in sorrow and pain that every one of the merrymakers was struck to the heart with the tragedy of it all. As the mother uttered cry after heart-rending cry, in a doleful sing-song, the crowd of hunters stared at her dumbly, and listened with rapt attention to her words:

> O Sier Lapalang! Jewel of my heart!
> I told you do not go
> to Ri Khasi, an alien land.
> Let us live in the plains
> and feed on the reed.
> But you said,
> my dearest pledge,
> I must look for jangew,
> my favourite food.
> But now, Jewel of my heart!
> Dark are the skies! Dark, too, the earth!
> The curved bow
> mounts your body,
> its rusty arrow
> dealing you a death blow.
> Man finds his sport,
> has his fun,
> But for me, there's nothing more
> under the sun.

They had never heard such stately mourning, such sincere protestations of deep love and devotion before. So affecting was the dirge, as it seemed to them, sung by U Sier Lapalang's mother, that there was not one man present in the gathering who did not shed a tear.

By comparison with that which they had just heard, these ancient Khasis found their own form of mourning inferior, comprised as it was of merely inarticulate wailings and ejaculations. They resolved to adopt the mode of the mother's lamentation, and since then, they have been known to couch their funeral songs in the most poetic of terms, voiced in the most haunting of notes.

Meanwhile, as U Sier Lapalang's mother sang her sad funeral song and wailed her agonizing lamentations, she burst her heart and followed her son to the other world.

The Child-devouring Stone

Once upon a time, in a village called Mawbeh, situated to the west of Mawkdok, halfway between Shyllong and Sohra, there lived in a small hut a poor young widow with her two sons. One was about six years old and the other was a mere toddler, not much more than a year. Being a woman alone, the widow had a hard time of it, and earned her living from day to day by taking on odd jobs, sometimes cleaning utensils and washing clothes in people's houses not too far away from her own home, and sometimes working in their fields.

Whenever she worked in other people's houses, the woman would leave her children at home. At such times the elder one would look after his brother, feeding him bananas and cuddling him to sleep. When the brother was asleep, the elder one would take care of a few odds and ends around the house, sweeping the floor, making up the bed and towards sunset, when his mother was due home, building up the fire and boiling hot water for her to wash her hands and feet. But when the woman had to work in the fields away from the village, she would take her two sons with her and keep them by her side as she toiled from morning to evening.

One bright sunny day found the young widow and her children on the path to a certain field on the outskirts of the village, which she had been contracted to plough. As they trod along, the widow carrying the tools in a bamboo cone called a *khoh,* and her son carrying the baby on his back, she fell to musing on her fate. No doubt, she thought, she led a dog's life, living from hand to mouth, working very hard and yet never having enough to feed her children and herself properly. And yet, on the whole, she was not unhappy. Looking at her young son and seeing how obedient he was and how clever he had become, she could not help feeling very proud, and indeed very happy, at the thought that soon he would grow up and she would have a man who would be breadwinner to the family.

She put her thoughts aside when she reached the field, and looked it over. How immense it was! Small mounds dotted the area and big boulders were lying scattered everywhere; she could see that her job would not be an easy one. But there was no help to it, so she decided to throw herself immediately into the task, and after carefully installing her sons and the lunch packs on one of the boulders, she said: 'Look after the baby very carefully, my dear. See that he doesn't fall down, and if he is hungry and starts crying, feed him the banana. I'm going to the bottom of the field.'

So saying, she gathered her spade and other tools and

went beyond one of the mounds to begin ploughing in earnest.

As soon as his mother went away, the young boy started playing with his brother, laughing merrily as he made him toddle up and down the boulder. But after some time at this game, he found the baby's feet suddenly stuck to the boulder. He tried to pull them out, but as he did so, the boulder seemed to suck them in more vigorously, so that the baby, now crying with all his might, was in no time knee-deep inside it. Aghast at this weird phenomenon, the boy shouted to his mother, 'Mother, Mother, the stone has swallowed the baby's feet!'

But the mother did not understand him properly. She vaguely heard something about a stone swallowing something and thought that her son was probably joking, or else being very foolish. So she replied evasively, 'Okay, son, I'll come as soon as I finish this part of the field.' She did not do that, however, and continued with her work.

Meanwhile, the boulder had swallowed the now unconscious baby up to its chest. At this the young boy thought of running to his mother and fetching her by force. But alas! He found his own feet stuck fast in the boulder. He started hollering all over again, 'Mother, come quickly, please come quickly! The stone has swallowed the baby to his chest and is starting on me! Come quickly, Mother!'

But the mother was too immersed in her work, and only replied, 'Wait, son, wait, I'm coming, just this one bit more.'

But the boulder did not wait. It devoured all of the baby, while working its way up the young boy's body. No longer seeing his brother, and feeling the terrible pain in his own legs, he called to his mother once again: 'Mother, Mother, the baby is no more. The stone has swallowed him up and it's swallowing me too! Mother, it is swallowing me too!'

But the mother said, 'Don't be afraid, son, I'll come as soon as I finish this piece.'

And so it continued for some time, with the son crying and shouting to his mother, while his mother shouted back reassurances even as the boulder devoured the boy as fast as it could, till, at last there was nothing left of him.

At about midday, the mother came to where she had left her children, with the intention of having lunch with them. But finding them nowhere on or near the boulder, she thought her son was playing hide-and-seek with her and so called out to him to stop playing and bring the lunch packs to her. When, after several calls, her dutiful son did not respond, she was seized with a sudden fear. What if the boulder had really swallowed them up! She had heard her son say something about the boulder, could it be that all the time he had been in genuine need of her help!

Thinking such thoughts only worsened her fear and she raved and called for her son again and again. But when no son answered her call, her fear turned into a terrible dread, and then an agonizingly painful realization that she had lost her children forever. Boulder or no boulder, she was convinced that something dreadfully wrong had happened to her sons. And this thought became so much stronger as time passed and evening approached that she cried and cried like someone who had lost her mind—as she probably had at that moment— and threw herself on the ground, tore her hair and bathed herself with dust from head to foot. After some time, however, she calmed herself somewhat, and quite resigned to her fate, appealed to God and the children to show some sign, that she might at least know what had happened to them.

'What can I do, my God, what can I do,' she lamented. 'I that have been cursed with such terrible misfortune? Let me suffer as long as I live, but at least let me be satisfied in knowing what happened to my sons. My children, as I have given birth to you and suckled you, let me see some sign so I know where you are and what terrible fate has parted me from you!'

As soon as she had said these words, she suddenly noticed, protruding from the flank of the boulder, the hand of her elder son, holding a piece of banana. She ran to him and pulled at his hand, but finding her strength not great enough, she sped off to the village to summon help.

On hearing what had happened, all the men of the village prepared for action, gathered their tools and picked up their sledge-hammers and pickaxes and hurried to the scene of the children's disappearance. There they immediately fell upon the boulder, hammering at its top, chiselling its sides and digging the ground beneath, trying to remove it from its moorings. But to their horror, the more they hammered, the more the boulder expanded, and the more they dug, the more it filled out. At last, quite spent and fearing for their own safety as well, the men gave up and returned to the village, a dejected and stupefied crew. In the face of such defeat, the best thing they thought they could do was to console the mother as much as possible, and that they did for many weeks to come.

When night had enveloped the whole earth and the wilderness had returned to its quiet once more, another boulder in the same field spoke out and condemned the cruelty of the child-devouring monster. This boulder so berated the other for being so cowardly as to touch the children of as hapless and harmless a woman as the young widow, that the wrongdoer grew quite mad and shot its neighbour in the flank with a large chunk of stone torn from itself. The shot caused a deep hole in the boulder, and from that hole spouted forth a jet of water that flowed day and night.

The two boulders still exist today, amidst dense undergrowth. From the flank of one stick out shapes like the hand of a child and a banana; and from the flank of the other gushes out a crystal-clear spring.

The Race Between Ka Ïew and Ka Ngot

Umïew and Umngot are two major rivers in the Khasi Hills, both springing from the Shyllong Peak and flowing towards the enormous plains of Bangladesh. But legend has it that many, many years ago the two had a different history in that they were the twin daughters of U Lei Shyllong, the god of Shyllong. As goddesses, the two were much acclaimed throughout the length and breadth of Ri Hynñiew Trep for their matchless grace and beauty and their apparent love for one another. For, in the world of spirits they were never seen apart but went everywhere in each other's company.

But unknown to many outside their closest circle of friends, the love that existed between the two sisters was not without its share of ups and downs, arising mostly out of the peculiar traits of the elder sister, Ka Ïew. Having, as the elder daughter, seen the sun and the moon first, Ïew was more presumptuous in knowledge, more conceited by nature and totally uncompromising in attitude. She was also bad-tempered and noisy, and always wanted to ride roughshod over everybody, including her own sister.

Ka Ngot, for that was how her younger twin was known, was more subdued, milder and pleasant, though not without a passion of her own which surfaced every now and then when her sister's impudence crossed the bounds of what was proper and decorous.

One bright sunny day in autumn, while the two young princesses were out strolling on the slopes of Shyllong Peak, enjoying the cool breeze and the magnificent scene of evergreen copses and hills tinged with gold by the autumn sun, the sisters' eyes strayed far away into the distant fields of Bangla. There they were, lying before them, reaching as far as the eye could see. There was apparently no end to them, and as the princesses gazed on, the water that collected in the numerous lakes shimmered in the sun so that the whole land seemed to twinkle with diamonds.

The hearts of both the maidens brimmed over with joy as they contemplated the sight. At that very instant a bold and adventurous plan presented itself to the excitable and impetuous nature of Ïew and she immediately gave voice to her thoughts: 'Say, sister, why don't we embark on an expedition to those shimmering lakes and unending valleys? Just imagine what new charms we may encounter! Staying on in these hills is boring!'

But Ngot shook her head. Though smitten as much as her sister by the exquisite beauty of the sight, she was far too sensible to give up the security and happiness of her home and follow a mere whim into such a remote land.

Ïew, on the other hand, saw nothing absurd in the scheme, and scoffed at her sister for being as timid as a rabbit and weak as a hen. 'Come on, you foolish girl,' she taunted, 'let's run a race and see who reaches those valleys first'.

At this Ngot grew alarmed. She said, 'Dear *Kong*,[1] if we must go, let us go together, without competing. The valleys are far and the way may be dangerous. It will be better if we stick together.'

But Ïew was not at all convinced. She flew into a rage, called her sister names, and said, 'If you are so damned afraid of the dangers on the way, let us turn into water and travel in the guise of rivers. But if you still say no to this, you are a coward and have no right to live like a goddess, but must turn into a rat and live in a hole like one.'

Now Ngot was truly provoked by her sister's scorn and insolence. She decided to take up the challenge, and so both of them, there and then, turned into rivers.

In keeping with her mild and temperate character, Ngot sought the soft and gentle ways in her journey, unmindful of the numerous twists and turns she had to take in doing this. Thus she glided gently till she reached a place in Bangladesh called Shilot, where she was supposed to meet her sister. In Shilot, however, she saw no sign of Ïew anywhere. She was surprised. Having made detours round many an obstacle, Ngot had lengthened her route a great deal and delayed her progress by many weeks. She had naturally expected her sister, therefore, to be already waiting there for her, with her boisterous laughter and her scorn. Not finding her there made Ngot extremely anxious. She changed course, veered towards Shatok and went on to Dwara in search of her sister. Not finding her there either, and now convinced that Ïew was nowhere ahead of her, Ngot swivelled round, and returned to look for her along the way she had come.

These serpentine curves form the most attractive part of

the river in its entire course, and when seen from a distance, with the sun's rays playing on the water's surface, the river looks strangely like silver. And that is why, to this day, people call it 'Wah Rupa Tylli', or the 'river of solid silver'.

All this time Ïew was preoccupied, fighting her own impediments on the course she had chosen. Proud and domineering as a tyrant, she aimed for her target like an arrow. In trying to reach Shilot by the shortest and quickest route possible, she ploughed her way through hills and valleys and swept away everything in her path, uprooting large trees, breaking stones, pushing boulders aside, cutting a path through jungles, jumping into deep ravines and digging tunnels into the ground. But in spite of her great strength, all this was slow labour, and without her knowing it, took a great deal of her time, for there was an obstacle almost every inch of her route.

And so it was not surprising that when she eventually rolled into Shella, near Shilot, she found Ngot far ahead of her. But Ïew was simply dumbfounded. To think that her weakling sister had put her in second place! It was intolerable! A trick of fate! Her pride deeply hurt, she raved, 'To suffer such damnable shame before the whole world! To be defeated by a mere child! How can I live on? Tell me, why *should* I live? I'll remain a river forever!'

Saying these words and cursing her fate, she cried and groaned, threw herself on the ground, and struck herself with such force that she splintered into five branches, called the Dwara, the Umtang, the Kumarjani, the Pasbiria and the Umtarasa.

On hearing about her sister, Ngot was grief-stricken. She blamed herself for everything that had happened and decided not to return home alone, but also remain a river by the side of her sister.

By and by the story of the two goddesses filtered into the

human world and people began to flock to these rivers as pilgrims. Ngot was especially esteemed as a superior stream, attracting non-Khasis from the plains to its banks to perform religious rites. The ancient Khasis themselves considered it an immoral act to ford this river or go across it on a bridge without first offering prayers to it, for the river was, after all, a modest victor and a goddess.

---

[1]Sister.

U Suid Tynjang

As described in 'The Lost Manuscript', the spirit world of the Khasis is essentially a three-tier system. At the head of this system is God, U Blei, the Creator, the Keeper, residing in heaven with all his spirits, and men and women who are not merely people departed from this world, but men and women who belong originally to heaven.

Below God there are the gods, *ki blei*, who are not simply the various manifestations of God, but constitute His representatives on earth, roughly corresponding to the Christian angels. Being His representatives, these gods are sometimes worshipped separately by the people, as in the case of U Lei Shyllong in Hima Shyllong or U Suitnoh in Hima Sohra.

After the gods come the lesser spirits, *ki puri* or fairies. Among these again there are two categories, the fair-skinned *puriblei*, or godly fairies, and the dark-skinned *puriksuid*, or evil fairies. The evil fairies are also simply called *ki ksuid* or demons.

U Ksuid Tynjang, or Suid Tynjang, belongs to this last category of demons and is said to haunt deep forests, ravines and precipices. His personal appearance is unprepossessing, lame and deformed as he is, his body covered in sores, the result of a skin continually chafed and scratched, for the demon is said to be tormented by a horrible itching disease, which can only be soothed by the vigorous scraping of a human hand.

It is for this reason that U Suid Tynjang comes out of his den at night, to hobble up and down jungle paths and lanes, carrying a kind of flambeau that blinks off and on with each clumsy step that he takes, and looking for a stray traveller that he can hold captive and force to rub his body, burning with such an irrepressible itch. To lure people to him, the demon has a shrewd strategy and often cries '*Kaw-hoit, kaw-hoit*', imitating the call humans make when lost in the wilderness or when attracting companions to them. Anyone so trapped by him is immediately ordered to '*kboh*' or scratch; but if the victim fails to satisfy him, the demon will do one of two things: tickle him to death with his claw-like hand or carry him to the brink of a precipice and leave him there to die of fright.

Later, U Suid Tynjang was said to have metamorphosed into a *jyrmi snam*, literally, 'bloodied creeper', a kind of tough, stout liana. The story that follows seeks to explain how this metamorphosis took place.

Once upon a time, in a small village to the north-west of the trading town of Sohra, there lived a poor family. Two of the girls, Ka Mai and Ka Deng, were still children, poised on youth, but being good, well-bred girls, they were already able to do many things around the house that might be expected only of adult females. And so, as their parents went to work with their elder brother, they would clean the house, wash the clothes, cook the family's meals, go to the jungles to chop wood and generally run the house as only two obedient and industrious girls could. The only thing the girls were not used to was shopping and that, too, because the market was far away in Sohra and had to be approached through lonely and wooded tracks.

One day their mother decided it was time for them to learn that chore too, and take it over from her. 'My dear daughters,' she said, 'you have been a great help working around the house. But you are fast attaining the age of adulthood and as young women you must also learn to shop for the family. Times are hard. I cannot afford to stay away from work even for a single day. Come next market day, you must go to Sohra with our neighbours and buy whatever is necessary for the house.'

In the marketplace called Ïewbah, the two sisters were astounded by the sight of so many people buying and selling. The shoppers were a noisy lot, shouting to each other, chattering away in the strange language of the market, with sellers peddling their different wares and buyers haggling over the prices. As they trailed after their friends from the village, the sisters gazed open-mouthed at all the articles of trade displayed in the stalls and spread on the ground before them.

'My God!' Mai thought. 'I had never dreamt that a market would be anything like this.' At one place they saw an assemblage of a variety of eatables. At another they saw fruits of all kinds; oranges, lemons, guava, litchi, and so on; at yet another they saw tons and tons of vegetables, fish and meat, notably beef and pork; and elsewhere they saw rows and rows of shining new clothes, utensils for the kitchen, implements for the fields, and indeed a conglomeration of all things useful and beautiful under the sun.

As they moved from place to place, the sisters did not know when or what to start buying. Everything attracted their attention; everything appealed to their fancy and seemed equally important. They were quite at a loss what to do, and finally they turned to their friends for help. But to their great astonishment, there was no one around them that they knew.

'God, Deng!' exclaimed Mai. 'Where are our friends? What is happening? We are lost!'

'Lost?' Deng said, in a bewildered tome. 'What shall we do?'

'There's nothing we can do but look for them. We must find them, Deng, we must...'

But Mai and Deng did not find their friends. The season being winter and the days being short, darkness soon enveloped the whole marketplace and flambeaux had to be lit. In desperation the two sisters gave up the search and left, hurrying away towards their village, hoping to overtake their friends on the way.

When they reached a wooded path through which they had to go, the two suddenly turned nervous and even contemplated turning back to the marketplace to seek shelter with anyone of the many people there. But at that very moment they heard someone call, 'Kaw-hoit, kaw-hoit.' They answered the call and were immediately answered back. Encouraged, they went into the woods, calling 'Kaw-hoit, kaw-hoit' all the while, and shouting to whoever was ahead of them to wait.

But that was a mistake for which they were to pay dearly. The voice belonged to U Suid Tynjang, and presently he appeared before them in all his hideousness. Seeing the horrible ape-like creature with the diseased skin of a mangy dog hobbling towards them, Mai and her sister shrieked and fell down in a swoon. The ksuid, however, soon revived them with his ticklish fingers and commanded them to kboh his scabby body.

The girls stared at the sores plastering him from head to foot and cringed away into a corner. To make matters worse, the stench emanating from the sores was so overpowering that the girls began to throw up violently. But for all that, they knew better than to refuse him indefinitely. They had heard many stories from their mother and the old ones in the village about this vile demon and his modes of punishment. Terrified, lest he should tickle them to death or place them on the brink of a fathomless gorge, they shut their eyes tightly and began to scratch his body vigorously. Up and down, and up and down, the ghastly hide they scratched till their hands were covered with the stinking pus and blood. But they forced themselves to go on till at last he fell off to sleep, soothed by the human touch.

As the ksuid slept, the sisters took turns scratching him. They dared not stop for fear of his awakening in anger. They knew from the stories that scratching would keep him happy and asleep, so they scratched away while they thought of a way to escape; for seeing him sleeping so profoundly, they had lost a little of their terror.

Mai, the cleverer of the two, soon hit upon an idea. 'Keep rubbing, Deng, keep rubbing,' she whispered. 'I'll go build a small fire in that corner and see what I can do to set ourselves free from this evil monster.'

When the fire was made up, Mai took out a dagger that her mother had given her earlier as a means of self-defence. She made it red hot and plunged it into the heart of the slumbering demon. But U Suid Tynjang did not writhe in pain as she had expected. He just seemed to shrink and grow smaller till finally he turned into a stout, round liana, lying curled on the ground like a snake. Terrified, the two fled from there as fast as their feet would take them, and did not stop running till they reached home safely in the morning.

That, however, was not the end of U Suid Tynjang. He was a supernatural creature and it was impossible to kill him. That day the creeper did not stir, but when darkness came, it moved, straightened and slowly assumed the original form of the ksuid. And that night the jungle resounded again with his 'Kaw-hoit, kaw-hoit' as he sought to snare yet another unwary traveller.

The Legend of Ka Lidakha

*I*n the nascent stage of its history, Ri Pnar, or the Jaiñtia Hills as it is known today, was only a disorganized cluster of villages without a *syiem*[1] or *hima*.[2] Each village kept to itself under its own administrators—elders and headmen—and consulted each other only in matters of trade. At that time there lived, in a hamlet called Umwi, a certain farmer known as Woh Ryndih, a man alone, spending most of his time toiling in his field from morning till night. Like all other men in the hamlet, however, he was very fond of hunting and fishing and often indulged himself in these pastimes whenever the opportunity presented itself.

One autumn morning, when

the sky was blue and the sun was brilliant, Woh Ryndih took up his fishing rod and went striding off in the direction of a nearby river called Waikhyrwi. At the river he took his position by the side of a large pool and settled down for a patient day-long stint. Very soon he could feel something nibbling at the bait and tugging at the line. He took the strain and pulled. Dangling at the end of the hook was a sizeable fish. This he caught with one hand, while with the other he plucked a reed-like plant, inserted it between the fish's gill and mouth to hang the fish on the low branch of a nearby tree and went back to fishing. But strangely, although he angled till the sun sank down below the western hills, he did not catch another fish.

When night came, Woh Ryndih returned to his hut with his fish, washed himself, made up the fire and cooked his meal. Then he took out the fish, put it inside a bamboo basket and left it dangling above the hearth to dry, meaning to boil it in the morning. But when morning came, he forgot all about the fish in his hurry to prepare for his day's work, and gathering his tools about him, left for his field without a backward glance.

When he came back in the evening, he was in for a big surprise. As soon as he opened the door, the warmth of the room embraced him like a comforting companion. He could see the fire burning at the hearth. The room was neat and clean, as if it had been swept recently, and when he looked at his pots, his food had already been cooked. He began to experience an eerie sensation of an unknown woman's presence in the house. But he brushed this foolish thought aside and guessed it must have been one of his nieces who had come to keep house for him during the day. Thus thinking, he ate his food, which was exceptionally delicious that night, and went to sleep.

But the following day the same story repeated itself.

Curious, he went to his sister's place to inquire if she had sent one of her daughters to his house that day and the previous one. The answer was no, she had not sent anyone to his house. That got him worried. Who was it, then, who had been keeping house for a lonely man like him? He could not think of any friend who would do something as inexplicable as visit his hut and do the domestic chores for him while he was away. No, he said to himself, this will not do. I must find out, by any means, just exactly who has been at my place. Thinking about it, he suddenly hit upon a plan and, comforted by it, retired to bed.

The next morning Woh Ryndih got ready for work and went to his field as usual. But once out of sight of his house he doubled back by another route and proceeded until he reached the back of his hut, where he settled down to wait and watch through a hole in the wall. He had a long wait, but finally, towards cooking time in the afternoon, he saw, to his utter amazement, a stunningly beautiful woman emerging from the fish in the basket. He watched her for some time, gazing with wide-eyed wonder at the unusual fairness of her skin, the brilliance in her eyes and the midnight blackness of her hair which cascaded down to her heels. He knew, of course, who she was. She could only be one of those fairies called *puri*, and from the loveliness of her face and the snowy whiteness of her *jaiñsem*[3] and her clothes, he guessed that she was a godly fairy or *puriblei*, and decided that there was nothing to fear from her. Even as he watched, he saw her sweep the floor, build up the fire in the hearth, clean the pots and prepare to cook the evening meal. But at this point his patience ran out and he hastened into the house to confront her.

As soon as the creature saw him and realized that she had been outwitted, she dashed towards the fish, meaning to shelter in its scaly skin once again. But, surmising rightly what she was about to do, Woh Ryndih jumped forward, snatched the fish from her grasp and threw it in the fire. Seeing her only means of escape destroyed, the strange maiden submitted herself to his powerful arms and answered his eager questions. 'Who are you? Where did you come from? And what do you want here?' he asked her.

'I am the daughter of a river nymph,' she said simply. I took a fancy to you as you sat fishing in the river alone, and I have come to be your wife.'

Hearing this frank admission, Woh Ryndih stared at her, speechless. Presently, his face broke into a smile and he promised to return her love in full measure by marrying her as soon as he had introduced her to his relations. But first she had to have a name. After briefly ruminating on the strange manner of his acquaintance with her, he decided to call her Ka Lidakha, or the 'one who came from a fish'.

After the introductions to the relatives were over and all the formalities had been completed, Woh Ryndih married Ka Lidakha. Soon, they had two daughters whom he named Ka Rytong and Ka Rnga. By and by, the two girls, being daughters of a nymph, grew up into a pair of exceptionally beautiful young women, who were constantly courted by the bravest and most handsome young men of the land. Consequently, when the time of their marriage came, the two had a very select band of admirers to choose from and naturally picked the best grooms in the field.

Having seen her daughters satisfactorily married off, Ka Lidakha determined to return to her pool. One day, while the family was sitting together, gathered round the hearth, she dropped her plan into their midst like a thunderbolt and said, 'My husband, dear daughters, it is time for me to return home. I can hear my mother and the others calling me back. From now on you must learn to live without me.'

Stunned into silence, everyone could only gape at her in

sheer disbelief. At length Woh Ryndih roused himself and said, 'My dearest wife, what foolishness is this? What are you saying? Surely you cannot mean what you said?'

When she affirmed that she did mean what she said, the daughters joined in the general protest and said, 'Our beloved mother, how can you leave us as orphans? Surely, you love us more than that! Forget this silly notion, stay on and let us be happy together.'

But despite many such earnest entreaties, and although they cried and pleaded with her for days, Ka Lidakha could not be persuaded to change her mind, for she argued that it was against the very nature of her being to stay indefinitely in the land of mortals.

When Ka Lidakha had gone back to her magic realm, Woh Ryndih tried to lead a normal life once more. But he found that impossible. For him it was as if the sun had suddenly set for ever. He lost all zest for life and began to pine away till one day, finding the weight of sadness unbearable, and the longing in his heart unquenchable, he visited the pool with his fishing rod once again, in a desperate attempt to win back his love. Win back his love he did, but in a manner quite contrary to all his expectations. As he sat by the pool, toying with his rod, suddenly, a big fish took his bait and pulled him headlong into the murky waters.

Woh Ryndih was never seen or heard from again, but his daughters and their families prospered and grew in strength. Being the descendants of a supernatural creature, they were looked up to and loved by one and all. In later years they became the proud mothers of many sons and daughters, who begot for them many other sons and daughters who spread throughout the land of U Hynñiew Trep. From Ka Rytong descended the clans of Sutong, Pala, Huwa and Ïongrem among others. From Ka Rnga two daughters were born who were named Ka Het and Ka Libon. From Ka Het descended the clan known as Lihet Sutnga, which later became the priestly clan of hima Sutnga; and from Libon descended the clan called Libon Sutnga, from which came the first syiem of hima Sutnga.

---

[1]King.

[2]State.

[3]Khasi outer garment comprising two long cloths of cotton, silk, etc., draped over the shoulders.

Ka Likai

*O*f all the tragic tales from the Khasi Hills, that of Ka Likai is perhaps the saddest and the most bizarre of them all, recounting the cruellest kind of suffering. Mother had chosen a perfect time to tell us the tale and how Likai's horrible fate had endowed the waterfall with the unhappy name, 'Kshaid Noh Ka Likai', which literally means 'The Plunge of Ka Likai Falls'. It was one of those dark pre-monsoon nights in Sohra, during the black month of April, when amidst the blinding flashes of lightning and the ear-splitting crashes of thunder tearing the black sky asunder, the wind howled and shrieked with madness and fury as it lashed the houses with pelting rain and hailstorm. Mother had said, 'The howling of the wind reminds me of the cries of Likai.'

Likai was a young widow from the ancient village of Rangjyrteh, about twenty kilometres to the west of Sohra, legendary capital of Hima Sohra, or traditional State of Sohra. The village was separated from the suburbs and sanctified groves of Sohra by a densely forested gorge at least three kilometres deep and six kilometres wide. At the bottom of the gorge runs a river known as Umiong or 'dark water' since a large portion of its cavernous length and breadth remained endlessly canopied under the shadows of the thick forest. The river empties itself into the gorges, hundreds of feet below, through a powerful soaring waterfall known then as 'Kshaid Umiong' or 'Dark Water Falls'. It was on a hill overlooking the waterfall that Rangjyrteh was located.

Though the village exists no more, it was in that distant past one of the most prosperous manufacturing and trade centres in the area, located as it was on a tableland, the meeting point of the villages situated in the many tangled and fertile ravines to be found in the Sohra country. As a result, the village became the most important wholesale market of the agricultural produce of the area, rivalling Sohra itself, to the great envy and unease of the *syiem*[1] of Hima Sohra and his council of ministers, who looked upon it as a threat, fearing the possible emergence of a parallel power hub. Added to this strategic location was the wealth of iron ore to be found in its environs, leading to a boom in the iron smelting industry, which drew business from as far away as Shilot, or Sylhet, in present-day Bangladesh.

Ironically, it was in the heyday of the village's prosperity that the tragedy of Likai was played out. It was as if the fate of the woman was a damning indictment of the spiritual depravity and the evil that lurked beneath the exterior of material well-being.

Likai was one of those unfortunate people who was

haunted by death throughout her life. Her parents had died when she was only a child and had left her nothing except her orphaned state and distant relatives, who had raised her out of a sense of duty, since Khasi society would not allow a clan to turn out any of its members who had suffered such bereavement. She was raised therefore, not as a flower but the way a weed is allowed to grow in the courtyard, through sheer idleness and negligence. But in spite of that, she had grown strong, and to the surprise of everyone, had blossomed like an orchid on a tree, and at the tender age of eighteen, had been wooed by every eligible bachelor in the village. But as soon as she had chosen a man to love, a man who had in turn loved her deeply, he died of a disease contracted during one of his business trips to Shilot. Could there be a woman as ill-favoured by fortune as Likai?

As the assistant of an iron trader, U Kynrem, her husband, had been working diligently to provide for her every need and to save a little for the time when he would be in a position to buy his own iron manufacturing works. But his sudden and early death ensured that Likai was left with nothing but grief, a poor hut standing among *ki dieng sohphie*[2] and a little girl child barely a year old.

What was she to do now? She was a grown woman with a child, no longer the responsibility of her relatives. She was supposed to fend for herself, but what could she do, especially burdened with a child that still had to be carried around?

Her friends consoled and advised her. 'Likai,' they said, 'we know that you have just lost a husband who was more than a husband to you. We know very well of your orphaned state. You had never known real love till your husband gave it to you. You had never lived in a real home till he provided it for you. You had never experienced peace till he brought it to you. He was the love, the shelter and the hope of your life. And now he is gone, you feel lost, like a boat tossed about the waves without its rower. You feel that your life has come crashing about your feet like a pile of rubble. But take heart, your husband has not died in vain. His spirit lives on in your daughter; let her be your new guiding force. Be strong, for her sake, work, scratch the earth, cut the wood, beat the stone. What does it matter? Let her be the new love of your life, the inspiration for your strength.'

With these and many such words Likai was comforted and by and by came to terms with her life. She began to take on odd jobs for a living—cleaning utensils in people's homes, sweeping their floors and courtyards, washing their clothes, fetching their water and ploughing their fields; and all this while carrying the baby strapped to her back by a strip of cotton cloth called *jaiñ-it*. When the baby became a toddler, she left her to play with her neighbours' children and earnestly began her profession as a piecemeal labourer, finally landing up as a carrier in one of the iron works.

In this way Likai toiled from morning till evening. It was a hard life, but not without its compensations, especially when she came home to the childish prattle of her four-year-old daughter. How lovely her Lasubon, her 'flower in the crown' was! How like her father—from the curls of her dark hair to the lively twinkle of her dark eyes, and that endearing smile, always lingering in the corners of her little chubby mouth. 'Come here, Lasu,' she would say, 'come give your Mei[3] a hug. Ah, so you enjoyed playing with Ri and Mai all day did you? And what about your Mei, did you miss her at all? You did? Oh, my little darling, I missed you too!'

Then she would wrap the child in her arms and rock her gently, tousling her hair, kissing her head and saying, 'You know, my little flower, when I come home and see you welcoming me so happily, I forget all about the aches in my bones, the pain in my muscles, the exhaustion in my body and soul. You are truly the image of your father. Yes my little princess, your father is in the house of God, U Blei. What he is doing there? He is persuading God to watch over us, he is telling Him to make you grow into the most beautiful woman in the whole hima, to make you forever happy and to let you marry the kindest and most accomplished man on earth. But run along now, go wash your little hands and feet by the trough; your Mei will cook some rice and dry fish for dinner.'

And after her daughter had gone running off to wash herself, she would gaze after her and pray to God to keep both of them safe, to guide them through life and grant them all their dreams and wishes in life.

This was how Likai spent her days—between her back-breaking work and her home, she did not have many close friends, and her social life was almost non-existent. But between her daughter and her memories, she did not pine for friends and was content to wear out her years in this dull yet tranquil state.

Life, however, had something else in store for her. Now that her daughter had grown into childhood, and Likai had regained some of her charm and youthfulness, young men began to flock to her hut again. Some came with the four-stringed *duitara* and flute to try to entertain her with song and music. But things were not the same for Likai. Their presence only reminded her of the nights of courtship with Kynrem, the magnificent, her husband, and how out of all those youths she had conferred upon him the traditional *kwai song* of betel nut and lime-smeared betel leaf, the sign of preferment over all the rest. Was she the cause of his death, or had God marked him out for an early end so that by choosing Kynrem she would become the unwitting victim of God's inscrutable ways?

With the support of Ka Deng, her nearest neighbour, who acted as her chaperone, Likai was able to discourage most of her new suitors by telling them frankly that she could never think of anything or anyone else again except her husband and the upbringing of his daughter whom she loved more than anything else in the world.

Almost all of them left her alone after that, for who would love a woman whose heart was fixated on the dead, and whose life was lived according to her notions of what would meet with the approval of that person and contribute to his happiness? As if the dead require the living to humour them!

There was one among them nevertheless, who persisted. His name was U Snar, 'the tough one', and he was none other than Kynrem's friend and old rival.

Unlike the rest, he knew the secret to Likai's heart. He visited her hut every night, but not to woo, as he told her, but to cheer her up a little and lessen the solitude of the evenings by a masculine presence about the house. Initially, Likai did not welcome his visits, particularly because he had been Kynrem's contender for her heart. It was only after a few persistent attempts on Snar's part that Likai began to tolerate his presence in her home. And this was because he never spoke of love or marriage and was so kind to her daughter, always bringing her something to eat or play with. Moreover, he never really bothered her since he would spend most of the evening entertaining Lasubon, who seemed to like him genuinely in turn. Snar would then leave as soon as the little girl went to bed on her little pallet of straw.

Soon this development was noticed by friends and neighbours. They understood what was going on, or at least they understood the intentions of Snar, and urged Likai to give new thought to the possibility of remarriage.

'Look,' said Deng, 'how can a woman live alone, with only a small child, in these uncertain times, when the village is being overrun by so many strangers—traders, merchants, dealers in iron, coal, limestone, and a myriad agricultural produce—from so many strange places? What if some of them, some lonely night, take it into their heads to force their way into your hut and do you and your little one some mischief? You need a man about the house.'

'Don't be foolish,' Likai responded. 'Who would dare do a thing like that when there are so many houses close to mine? Besides, I always bar my house at night.'

'Ah, have you forgotten what happened just a few weeks ago at Bihrit's? Don't you remember how some out-of-town *nongshohnoh*[4] had tried to break into her hut in the middle of the night? And mind you, this was in spite of the fact that there are menfolk in that house.'

'I'm not afraid of any nongshohnoh,' Likai persisted. 'Bihrit is in the suburbs, I'm not. All I have to do when threatened is to shout. My compound may be enclosed by the embankment and young trees that Kynrem had planted, but it is flanked by neighbours. I don't have anything to worry about there.'

'Likai,' chipped in Ka Nah, her other neighbour, 'it's not only a question of safety we are talking about here. There's a man visiting your house every night. He is obviously head-over-heels in love with you. How can you simply ignore the fact and treat him as if he were merely your daughter's pet?'

'But Nah, you know very well that I cannot bear the thought of another man taking Kynrem's place. Kynrem is special; he is my first and only love. He is my redeemer; he lifted me out of my orphaned state. He is my lodestar, my *maji*, the helmsman of my life. Death has not parted him from my heart. The very idea of another man touching me gives me the shivers.'

'You are being stupid and selfish,' accused Deng angrily. 'How can you allow your life to be oppressed and regulated by a dead man? Have you given any thought to the welfare of your child? You are working very hard for her sake! And yet, where are you leaving her when you go to work? Do you think it is fair to your daughter to let her grow like a plant in the wilds? Do you think she will grow up into a nice and proper young woman if she is reared like untended goats and cattle? That's what you are doing to her by leaving her day in and day out with your neighbours. And yes, I for one cannot play nursemaid to your daughter forever. I have my work to do, my own kids to look after.'

Nah, too, so readily and so wholeheartedly agreed with Deng in her threats that poor Likai became thoroughly dejected. 'All right,' she replied. 'But supposing we are right in assuming Snar's love for me, and supposing I consent to marry him, how would that solve Lasubon's predicament? I would still have to go to work and she would still have to sit the day out with her neighbours.'

Sensing their victory, the two matchmakers softened their tones and became conspiratorial. 'Listen Likai, we know for a fact that Snar is desperate for your love,' Deng revealed. 'In fact, he has enlisted our help in persuading you to allow him to propose to you. Look, he loves you, and that is beyond doubt because he had been one of your very first suitors along with Kynrem. And most importantly, he loves your daughter...isn't that obvious from the way he endears himself to her in all sorts of ways? Where would you find such a man, a true lover and a devoted father?'

'About Lasubon, don't worry about a thing; we have discussed that with him too. As you know, he is the only son of a rich business family. He is now helping his father run the limestone and iron quarries. When you marry him, you won't have to work at all. If you want too, you can take a job in one of the rich households, work there for an hour or two and return home to Lasubon. For that matter, Lasubon could accompany you to your workplace so there would be no need for her to be alone any more. What do you say, eh? Aren't things working out rather neatly?'

Thus, with the help of the matchmakers, Snar was able to convince Likai to accept him as her husband and also to persuade the headman of the village to sanction their cohabitation. This, Snar explained to Likai, was only a temporary arrangement since his parents did not agree to the marriage. 'But don't worry about them, dear Likai, they will come round sooner or later. Parents always do.'

To her own surprise, Likai did not find her new life so distasteful. She gave up her punishing labour at the ironworks and helped only for an hour or so at the house of a rich merchant, mainly washing clothes at a nearby stream flowing south-east to the river Umiong. If truth be told, Likai was rather happy at the new arrangement since it afforded her the hitherto unthinkable luxury of being together with her beloved Lasubon, who now followed her wherever she went. Snar, too, was good to her and treated her daughter in the same gentle and generous manner, although many a night he was dislodged from Likai's bed by the cries of the little girl for her mother.

Then one day, barely two full moons after their life together began, Snar came home in the middle of the day. He said, 'My parents have thrown me out of the family business. It seems they haven't forgiven me. But don't worry, Likai, this is only a temporary setback. I will look for a job elsewhere.'

Days became weeks, but Snar did not get employment anywhere. Likai found this hard to believe, yet maybe, as he had said, his parents had something to do with it; after all, they were influential people. In the meantime, the situation in the house was getting worse. There was no rice even for two meals a day, not to speak of meat, fish and vegetables. Finally, not wanting to see her little girl go hungry, Likai volunteered to go back to her old harrowing job at the ironworks.

Things were almost back to where they had started. Lasubon stayed home with Snar, who was still looking for employment, and Likai went to her now even more arduous work. Her employer was expanding his business and was dealing directly with traders from Shilot so that porters like her had to go all the way to Mawmluh, south of Sohra, to deliver the ingots. For Likai, this meant leaving home before daybreak and getting back just before nightfall.

Only this time, instead of the cries of joy and welcome, she would be received with a barrage of complaints from Lasubon. One day the little girl said: 'Mei, Papa brought home many strangers. They were drinking and they said bad things about me, and about you. I don't want to stay home. I want to go with you to work.'

Likai enfolded her in her arms and said, 'Hush, my little love, don't say things like that. I will speak to your Papa.'

There was no chance to speak to Snar that day, however, for as soon as he heard Likai arriving he came out, head bent, and not looking at his wife, said, 'I'm going out to meet a potential employer. I'll be home late. Don't wait for me. Leave the door ajar.'

And so the moon waxed, the moon waned—day after day Likai came home to more and more allegations and complaints, and night after night she listened to more and more drunken and abusive clamour. When Likai tried to talk to him, cajoling him into looking for a job seriously and putting an end to his frustrated drinking, he would push her face back and hiss, 'Oh, you want to quarrel in the middle of the night, do you? You really want the neighbours to know what a bad man I am, is it? Job, job, job. Looking after your damned daughter is more than a full-time job. Now leave me in peace and go to sleep. If you can't get up for work tomorrow, how will we eat?'

One day, Likai arrived home to the shrieks of a child in

pain and the dull recurring thuds of something heavy hitting against something soft. It was a snarling Snar beating Lasubon with a thick stick as if she were a pile of straw, while his bleary-eyed and drooling-mouthed friends were cheering him on. The child was howling and cowering in a corner, lifting her small hands in a pitiable attempt to ward off the thumping blows.

At this painful spectacle Likai flew into a mad rage. She went to the hearth, picked up a burning wood and attacked Snar and his drunken friends with it. She followed them as they fled outside, shouting terrible oaths after them: 'Why did you do this, you senseless creatures? Why did you have to thrash my poor baby as if she were a piece of sackcloth? Look at her swollen little hands and feet! Look at her bruised face and blistered body, you brutes. What did she do to deserve all this, you good-for-nothings?'

'I didn't do anything, Mei,' cried Lasubon. 'I only said I didn't know how to buy *kyiad*.'

'What? You miserable wretch, how could you ask an innocent little child to go and buy your cursed liquor? Have you no heart? You came to my house with big promises, but you are living like a parasite. Are you not satisfied with turning me into your slave that you now want to turn my poor child into your kyiad-bearer too? I married you in the hope that you would take good care of my daughter but this is what you do, you shameless polluter! And you, you scum and connivers! Get out of my house and never come back!'

Meanwhile, Snar, who was swaggering about drunkenly, kept pointing his forefinger at Likai and muttering, 'So you want me to take good care of your daughter? Let me take care of her right now.' With this, he lunged at Lasubon, only to meet with a blow to the head from the burning log that Likai was holding. 'Ow!' he yelped, 'what are you beating me for? I only want to take care of your daughter. You just wait. You think I'm bad, I'll prove you wrong. I'll take such good care of your daughter that you will never have reason to complain ever again.' And so he kept on muttering incoherently till he was dragged to bed by the threatening onlookers.

When things quieted down, Deng and Nah, who had witnessed the whole scene, came to commiserate. Nah shook her head in amazement: 'I never thought he could be so rotten,' she observed.

But Deng disagreed: 'I don't think you should take it so seriously. Kyiad can do strange things to men, but that doesn't mean they are not good people at heart. Take Father of Shan, my husband, for instance. When he drinks he becomes a real tiger. Otherwise, as you know, he is as harmless as a goat. The thing is how to get them to stay away from liquor, and to understand what drives them to it. In my opinion, Likai, I think you are pampering your girl just a little too much. Perhaps, it is that which Snar resents—you know how jealous stepfathers can be? Just think about it: would you have reacted the way you did had it been Kynrem beating up Lasubon? But mark my word, when he wakes up tomorrow he'll be a different person. He did say he'll show you he is not bad.'

'Maybe Deng is right,' Likai said to herself. 'Next market day, which is a half-working day, I'll really have a heart-to-heart talk with Snar,' she resolved.

The next morning before leaving home, Likai, as always, bade her daughter goodbye and said, 'Today, if you don't want to stay at home you can go and play at San Deng's, all right?'

'All right, Mei,' Lasubon responded happily, 'I'll do that, *khublei*, goodbye, Mei. Come back soon.'

That afternoon, when Likai returned home she found the house unusually quiet. Lasubon did not come running to her as she used to do. As Likai washed her hands and feet in the water trough, she called out: 'Lasu! Lasubon! Where are you, *khun*, daughter of mine?'

Nobody answered. She went to her nearest neighbour, Deng. 'Have you seen Lasubon?' Likai asked anxiously.

'I saw her with the kids earlier. But I haven't seen her since. She must be playing around here somewhere. Maybe at Nah's,' Deng replied casually.

There was smoke rising from the hut, so Snar must at least be close by, reasoned Likai. Even the door was not barred. 'Yes,' Likai mused, 'they must be somewhere nearby. Let me go inside anyway. *Aree!* Surprise of surprises! Snar has cleaned the house and cooked the food! The blow I gave him in the head has done wonders, it seems. He must have felt bad about the quarrel yesterday and is trying to make up for it. Mmm, what an aroma! She lifted the lid off the vessel. Aha! Chicken curry, or is it a young pig? Delicious fragrance! From where did Snar get this wonderful meat?' She picked up a piece and put it in her mouth. 'Very tasty. Somebody in the village must have called in the faith healers and must have had to sacrifice a piglet or a rooster. Yeah, that must have been it; they must have distributed the meat, for after all, it has to be finished within a single day. Ah, I'm dying of hunger. Lasubon must have eaten already; yes, some rice has been scooped from the pot. Let me also eat now and look for her afterwards. There's still some light, let her play a little while longer.'

Thus, her appetite whetted by the unusual fare, Likai fell upon her food with gusto. When she had had enough, she went out to wash her hands, then stood back to rub her belly, and even burped a little with delight. What a hearty meal, she thought, all I need now is a nice little pack of *kwai* to round it off.

Inside, as she used to do after a meal, she reached for the round bamboo basket, the *shangkwai*, where they kept the betel nuts, betel leaves, lime and tobacco, needed for a preparation of kwai. She pulled the basket towards her and placed in on her lap, only to spring up, recoiling in terror. For a while she stared stupidly at the objects in the shangkwai, until a loud and piercing cry of '*Wow rap!*' broke out from the very depths of her being. It was a heart-rending cry for help, a cry from the pit of despair, so loaded with anguish and torment, so shrill with horror that it flew over the hut to smite the darkening roofs with such threatening foreboding that an enormous shudder rose from the entire village.

Likai's world came crashing down. Heaven and earth darkened in an instant, and she was aware of nothing but the little hands, from the wrist down, the sweet little hands of her sweet little child. Yes, they were Lasubon's. She would know them anywhere, dead or living, whole or in pieces. There they lay with the betel nuts in the basket before her, still longing for her loving touch. In a wink she understood the foul crime that the unseen power, that unpitying and unjust arbiter of her fate had seen fit to make her commit, as the ultimate recompense for a life badgered by grief, suffering and bereavement. Yes, she understood now: that vicious savage of a stepfather had cut the child to pieces, prepared a curry from her flesh and had trapped her into eating her very own daughter, her very own soul, her very own life.

'Wow rap,' she shrieked again and threw herself on the floor, howling like a dog in pain. She tore her hair loose, rent her clothes off, and tore at her belly, retching and writhing on the ground like a butcher's sow in the last painful throes of its life.

People came rushing to her hut, agog with excitement and apprehension: 'Why, what's wrong? Light a lamp...what happened?'

When they saw Likai, squirming naked on the floor and weeping huge violent sobs that racked her whole body, they admonished her, 'Why are you doing this to yourself? Are you mad? What is it that has happened that you should behave in such a manner?'

Likai only wailed more shrilly: '*Wow Mei!* My Mother!' she called out. 'What life is this you have given me? What wrong have I done? What misdeeds, what transgressions, what sacrilege have I committed that I should be marked out for this abominable crime?

'But what happened? Tell us what happened!'

'Wow Mei! The fiend! The monster! He has killed my daughter, he has cooked her flesh, he has made me eat it. Wow Mei! What shall I do?'

On hearing the confession, the crowd sent up an uproar. While the women, who were now weeping themselves, tried to calm and console Likai, the headman called out angrily, 'Hey, ho! You, the menfolk, you, the real sons of your mothers! Let us go and hunt down this demon, this offspring of Thlen! [5] This very night we shall purge the village of this evil!'

At these words, Likai suddenly snatched the long, hooked knife that was hanging from the wall, the very knife that was perhaps used to chop up Lasubon, and vowed, 'Of course! Hunt him down, that's what I'll do.'

With the wood-cutting knife in hand, she ran outside crying, 'Where is he, where is that child killer? Where is that cannibal? I'll avenge you yet, my child!'

The men and women followed her through the dark lanes, calling to her, trying to hold her back. But nobody could go near her because she would swing the knife at anyone who came too close. Finally, they reached the suburbs of the village, on a hill looking out over the Umiong waterfall. Exhausted by her mad rush, Likai, still holding the knife, fell to the ground, beating it with her hands and shrieking like one who has truly lost her senses: 'Oh, my child! My black-eyed bloom! My soul! My most beloved on earth! Flesh of my flesh! Blood of my blood! Bone of my bone! I cannot even find the brute who has done this to you; who has done this to us. Your flesh is churning in my stomach and I cannot even find the demon. What use, my flower in the crown of queens, what use is my living without you, in shame and torment...? How stupid of me! You wished me "khublei" this morning—you said, "Thank you, Mei, farewell and God bless you"—and I did not recognize it as your last greeting! I am an ill-omened companion of death. At the mere touch of my flesh, my parents died, my husband died, and now you, the very purpose of my life. What is the point, then, in living in this accursed place that dispenses only sorrow and incessant tears, and where fortune scatters only the seeds of misery and death? Yes, death is the only true and constant comrade of my wretched life. Death, yes only in death will I ever find my peace.'

And with that she sprang up and dashed towards the waterfall, all the while crying forlornly, 'Why? Why did he perpetrate this foul deed upon me? What dreadful wrong have I done to him? Why did God allow such evil to happen to me? Why? Why...why...why...'

Those were the last words that were heard before Likai plunged herself headlong into the waterfall, which would bear the tragic burden of her name for all time to come.

Meanwhile, Snar, who was all this while skulking among the trees by the edge of the Umiong forest, took a last look at the unfolding scene. He gnashed his teeth and with a grim smile turned away into the dark fastnesses of the forest, never to be heard of again.

The story of Ka Likai spread far and wide and moved to tears all those who listened to it. But for the syiem of Sohra and his ministers, it was an opportunity they had been long waiting for. The syiem convened the dorbar hima—the council of state to which every adult male from the provinces and villages within the hima was entitled to attend—to discuss the ghastly incident at Rangjyrteh and to decide upon the fate of the village, which had allowed such boundless evil to take place. After a careful day-long deliberation, during which many viewpoints for and against were taken into account, the council eventually resolved by a majority sanction to derecognize the village of Rangjyrteh. The inhabitants of the village were advised to disperse to surrounding settlements, and the Lyngdoh Hima, the chief priest of Hima Sohra, was instructed to perform sacrificial rites at the Rangjyrteh market so that the evil would not repeat itself.

---

[1] Traditional Khasi king.

[2] Trees with small sour-sweet fruits.

[3] Mother.

[4] Killers in the employment of Thlen-keepers, whose business is the hunting of men for their blood. A Thlen is a man-eating serpent. See 'The Man-eating Serpent, U Thlen'.

[5] See 4 above.

U Manik Raitong

U Manik Raitong, or Manik the Wretched, is celebrated as the archetypal lover and the dispenser of the tradition of love and music in Khasi society. He lived, some time in the remote past, in the capital of one of the biggest Khasi states, or himas, in those days,[1] located in the contemporary Ri Bhoi district to the north of the Khasi Hills towards the Assam border. He was an orphan from youth, a young man all alone in the world, who had lost not only his family but also all the members of his clan. Yet he was neither poor nor wretched in the material sense, for he had inherited all the property of his clan, which comprised a spacious hut at the outskirts of the town and large tracts of cultivable land, bordering a nearby village.

At that time Manik spent almost all his time in his extensive and partly wooded fields. He would leave at third cockcrow and return at nightfall to a lonely hut, never enlivened by the company of friends, for he had none.

In the fields, where he grew a little paddy, a little millet, a little of this and a little of that, his routine was never rigorous. He would work on a furrow or two till his midday meal and then retire to the hills and the groves to listen to the songs of birds and the melodies of insects in the bushes. As he often told himself, he had no need to work hard, having only himself to support. His sole ambition was to learn how to recreate the countless sounds of Nature, which had strangely brought such restful consolation to his bruised soul.

It was while he was wandering about in this manner that Manik met a remarkably beautiful girl in a neighbouring village. He had strayed absently into the fringes of the village and was going down to a *shyngiar*, a spring spouting from a length of split bamboo, for a drink when he bumped into the girl emerging from another lane.

Surprised, they stared at each other and then blurted out at the same time, 'Who are you?'

A nervous laugh followed...the girl turned to proceed down the lane. Then Manik, like a man in a dream, and afraid that his dream might come to an abrupt end, blurted out again: 'Wait...'

She waited, looking him full in the eye as if daring him to speak his mind. Manik gazed at her, enthralled. He had never seen such a beauty before. Here he was, looking for the rare and tuneful strains of Nature and finding instead a rare and beguiling flower. Not that she was dressed differently from the girls he had seen in the fields. Like them, she was wearing a *jaiñsem*[2] over her sarong skirt, and like them, she even had, slung across her shoulder, a *ïarong*, one of those small net purses woven from the thread of pineapple leaves so common among working women. Nonetheless, he could see that she was no ordinary woman. She had about her an apparent elegance, a confident grace that no clothes, however common, could ever obscure.

Manik was even more fascinated by the peach-blossom of her face. Her thick black hair, pulled back firmly and tied in a bun at the back of her head, only intensified the effect of her cerise complexion, her luminous dark eyes and her smiling thorn-berry red lips so that she seemed to be aglow like early sunrise.

'Forgive my rudeness,' he finally said when he saw her blushing uncomfortably under his intense gaze. 'I'm sorry to embarrass you like this...you are so...I...I have never seen you before.'

Seeing him ill at ease himself, the girl giggled happily and said, 'But we have been watching you every day. You never seem interested in anything except the singing of birds and the loud chirping of the cicadas. Are you a poet?'

'No, I'm only trying...'

'Someone's coming,' interrupted the girl, 'I have to go.' And with that she turned towards the shyngiar.

Manik shouted after her, 'Will I see you again?'

'If you want to see me, come to my house tomorrow,' the girl called back. 'Ask for the house of the Lyngskor.'

'What?' Manik thought. 'The Lyngskor? Is she the daughter of the Lyngskor, the chief in the king's council of ministers? No wonder she looks high-born. Anyway, Lyngskor or no Lyngskor, I will go. After all, she invited me...and come to think of it, I'm not so badly off myself.'

The next day Manik tried to appear as respectable as he possibly could in his clean work clothes, since he did not want to wear formal ones lest he drew undue attention. He presented himself at the house of the Lyngskor late in the afternoon and was received by the mother herself, who said:

'Oh, so you are the man my daughter has fallen for? No wonder...you are so well turned out.' She called to an attendant: 'Please bring us the *shangkwai*...yes, the betel nut basket.' Then, turning to Manik, she resumed, 'Now tell me about yourself.'

Manik introduced himself.

'What! You are the sole surviving son of Ka Phrin and U Sherin! Please wait here,' she said and left the surprised Manik to himself.

In the kitchen she reprimanded her daughter and told her not to bring the shangkwai to the main room. 'And all of you,' she said, addressing her entire family, 'stay out of sight. What I have to tell the young man is not for your ears. You are lucky your father is not here.'

Back in the main room she addressed Manik in peremptory tones: 'I'm terribly displeased that you, a miserable orphan, could be so presumptuous as to court the daughter of a Lyngskor. What have you got to offer her except misfortune and perhaps, God forbid, untimely death? Don't you know what people are saying about you? You carry with you the touch of death. You have caused the death of your parents, your family and your entire clan; and now you want to bring such ill luck into my house too? When Ka Phrin, your mother died, she left in your care her only daughter. What happened to her? You are a death dealer. Your name shall never be spoken in this house. Your presence here shall never be permitted. Now go, cast your ominous shadow elsewhere.'

Poor Manik, his love had ended as soon as it had begun. He did not even know the girl's name, but what was the use of knowing it? He had not realized till then that there was so much hatred for him in this world. How could he have caused the death of his parents, family and clan? How had he been a death dealer? It had always seemed to him that God and the dead had been cruel to him by deserting him in this unfriendly world, but now that same world was trying to turn things upside down by putting the blame on him.

'Ah, my dearest sister, you were the last to go,' he thought aloud to his absent sibling. 'How I had tried to save you! Surely everyone knows and remembers how much it meant to me that through you, our clan would live on and prosper. When you fell ill, I had collected every plant and herb known to man, for your cure. I had brought all the shamans, the healers, the diviners from every nook and cranny of the hima, so that they could plead for your life with their ritual egg-breaking and their sacrificial roosters. I had desperately wanted you to live so that you might in turn be my companion and caretaker. But the world is blaming me for your death.

'I'm like an animal in its lair, sad and lonely, yet the moment I try to come out, people chase me off and hound me out as a dirty and dangerous creature. Alone then, I shall live from now on, alone as long as I breathe, and since I am treated like an outcast, like an outcast shall I live. I shall dress in sackcloth and dust myself from head to foot with ash from the hearth of my burnt-out life. Let me give the world a reason to denounce me as a pariah. Let it shun and leave me alone. But away from meddling eyes, in the friendship of the night, let me be pure and spotless. Let me be true to myself. Let me be true to my quest. Let me speak with the musical sounds, the healing tones of Nature.'

If truth be told, many a young woman would have been only too happy to be courted by Manik. He was young, handsome and a man of property. Surely, since everybody had to die one day, the thought of future death would not have been as important to young women in love as their present well-being. But who was to tell Manik that the feeling of one indignant mother did not represent the collective truth of the society, and would not necessarily repeat itself?

It was from that time that Manik began to appear to the world in sackcloth and ashes. That was how he walked through the lanes of the town, whistling to himself or practising with the seven-mouthed *sharati*, the long slender flute he had invented, carved from seasoned *shken*, the small-stem bamboo. That was how he went to his fields and roamed the woods in search of new tunes for the instrument which had become his only true companion. But unknown to the world, he waited for the gloom of evening. That was when he bathed; he dressed in his best clothes; he played through the night, sharing with the crickets the sad story of his life.

It was from that time that the world came to call him Manik Raitong, Manik the Wretched, Manik the Forsaken.

And so Manik lived the life of a recluse for many years, oblivious of what was going on in the world. He was ignorant of and uninterested in the affairs of the town. It was as if life had passed him by completely, and except for the occasional jeers of the town's children, who branded him 'a mad man playing mad music', he was completely ignored as if he did not exist at all. There were tremendous changes in the world around him, but he remained blissfully unaffected by them.

A young syiem, a strong ruler and powerful warrior, had taken over the governance of the hima. Under his leadership the hima, and consequently its capital, were growing in fame and prosperity. The syiem had won many battles and annexed many territories. The hima had expanded on all sides but especially towards the north where its territories extended far into the plains of Assam from Goalpara in the west to the Cachar Hills in the east. To govern these territories, the Syiem appointed many *syiem raijs*, or provincial kings, who reported directly to him at the capital in Ri Bhoi.

The syiem was truly a hero, loved and respected in the whole hima, and feared throughout the length and breadth of the Khasi and Jaiñtia Hills, known in those days as Ka Ri U

Laiphew Syiem Bad U Khatar Doloi or the Land of the Thirty Kings and a Dozen Dolois. What enhanced his image as a hero was the fact that he was still a bachelor at thirty, a bachelor who was the dream of every young woman and whose marriage was a subject of endless debate and speculation.

The syiem was, of course, in no hurry to marry. He had no desire to settle down and grow old just yet. He was a man of action whose real thrill in life came from being in the thick of a battle and whose ambition was to go down in legend as the greatest conqueror and nation builder of the Khasis.

His mother, however, had different plans for him. She realized that he was living a dangerous life and wanted to curb his restless spirit by diverting some of his energy towards the responsibilities of raising a family. Besides, as she told the syiem, she would like to see him happily married off before she grew too old to perform her part of the nuptial rites.

Following the queen mother's wishes many matchmakers were engaged to look for the most eligible bride in the hima. But as it turned out, their services were not really required, for the syiem had fixed his fancy upon Ka Lieng Makaw, the only unmarried daughter of the Lyngskor, who had been introduced to him by none other than the Lyngskor himself.

Lieng Makaw became officially betrothed to the syiem after the engagement ceremony called *kyntiew synjat* was performed. The wedding itself was fixed for six full moons after that, to allow the entire hima time to gear up for the grand event. The invitation was relayed to every part of the land through special messengers, and soon after, weeks before the occasion, representatives from villages and provinces arrived with gifts of goats, cattle, pigs, poultry, rare birds and wild animals captured for the purpose, besides basketfuls of paddy, millet, maize, fruits and foodstuff of every description. They poured into the capital town from every direction and

occupied every empty space in the suburbs, singing and
dancing to the accompaniment of the raucous pipe music of
ka tangmuri and the booming sound of *ki ksing*, the big and
small drums.

On the wedding day everyone was curious about the
mahadei-[3]to-be. Had their syiem chosen the right woman for
his wife? What did she look like, to win the approval of such
a king? Was she fair? Was she tall? Did she have the grace,
the refinement, the sterling qualities required of a true
mahadei of the people?

It was for this reason that the wedding was held in an
open field to let all the citizens have a glimpse of the bride.
The ceremonial rites were conducted by the Lyngdoh Hima,
the chief priest, in the presence of the ministers, the syiem
raijs, the nobles and representatives of the Dorbar Hima, the
Council of State, and countless other dignitaries from
neighbouring himas.

And yes, Lieng Makaw was everything that the people
expected, and more. She was dressed in a brilliant yellow
velvet blouse over which were suspended, crosswise, a pair of
chaste white *dharas* on mulberry silk jaiñsem with gold
designs near the hem just above the flowing tassels. Over and
above them she wore, draped over her shoulders, a milky
satin cape. On her feet was a pair of slippers made of specially
treated deerskin. On her arms were bracelets, bangles and
armlets of solid gold inlaid with rubies. Her necklace was a
konopad made of flattened gold and adorned with topazes and
rubies, her earrings were dangling gold leaves, her crown was
a tiara of gold and diamonds to hold her ample hair, which
was swept back and left flowing loose down her spine like a
cascade of black silk.

There she was, sitting beside the majestic syiem in the
specially decorated, gem-studded love-seat. To say that she
was beautiful was to understate the truth. She was the snow

on the summit of Ki Mangkashang,[4] kissed by the golden sunlight of the afternoon. She was the goddess of the mountains, a nymph, pure and sparkling like the pearls and gemstones found in magic depths. The revellers heaved a collective sigh of happiness, and bunches of them broke into dance and sang paeans to the spectacular queen consort.

Lieng Makaw moved to the palace of the syiem, an exception the matrilineal Khasis allow for their rulers. Since normally a married Khasi woman would never go to settle in her in-laws' house, it was hard to describe Lieng Makaw's feelings at that moment. She was living in a strange place (not exactly with the in-laws but in a palace in the same compound), bound to a man she hardly knew, a man, moreover, she had not fallen in love with at first sight. But that man was also a king, regal, celebrated and revered. It would be false to say she was unhappy; nevertheless, it would also be untrue to say she was delighted.

Adjusting to the new life with its protocol and decorum, its duties and responsibilities, was rather awkward for her, for she was used to the freedom of the hills. Her new family assured her that she would grow accustomed to her altered circumstances with the guidance and inspiration of the syiem. And so, perhaps, she *would* have got used to things, and grown to love the syiem dearly in the bargain, but for the fact that the syiem never seemed to have much time for her.

Barely a week after the wedding, the syiem announced: 'My dear Mahadei, there are rumblings of discontent in my provinces in the plains. I have to head there immediately. I cannot risk a full-scale rebellion on my hands at this point. No, I cannot take you along, it would be too dangerous. Besides, I don't know when I'll be back. I'm leaving tomorrow with the Lyngskor and some of my most trusted ministers and swordsmen. I have appointed a *syiem khynnah*[5] to administer this part of the hima in my absence. Please look after the affairs of the palace. I don't want any indiscipline among the servants. Keep everyone on a tight leash. My mother and sister will help you carry out your duties in a manner befitting a mahadei.'

That night, Lieng Makaw could not sleep for a long time. 'Why is he leaving me alone so soon after the wedding?' she asked herself. 'Why is he avoiding me? Is his work that important? Why can't he take me along? Could it be that dangerous? How can I live here without him? I'm still almost a stranger here...'

As she was moping in this fashion, she suddenly heard a strange, almost weird, sound carried on the wings of the night breeze. What mournful music, she thought. I have never heard anything like this before...it cannot be the raucous tangmuri, which is played only during festivals and occasions...nor is it the moan of the three-stringed duitara...what could it be?

The music seemed to creep in from cracks in the wall to tug at her heart-strings. She sat up and wakened the syiem, 'Pa'iem! Pa'iem![6] Listen...can you hear that?'

The syiem woke up and listened. Just at that moment, however, there was a sudden lull and the music stopped. 'It must be the wind,' the syiem said. 'Go back to sleep.'

By and by Lieng Makaw dozed off. Just before she fell asleep she thought she could hear snatches of the music again but could not keep her eyes open and slept almost against her will.

The syiem departed at third cockcrow, accompanied by his most intimate advisers and a large number of fighting men including some of the fiercest swordsmen and the most accomplished archers in the hima. Lieng Makaw felt forlorn. Despite the syiem's justification of his action, she felt vaguely, inexplicably let down and unwanted. She was so depressed by this desertion, as it seemed to her, that she moved about the palace as if she were in a trance. And thus she continued for many days, an outsider and alone. Her loneliness owed itself, in no small measure, also to the indifference shown to her by the syiem's family living in the ancestral mansion at the centre of the palatial compound.

One day, towards nightfall, after a perfunctory dinner, she found her loneliness so overpowering, her sense of neglect so unbearable that she literally ran out of the suffocating confines of the palace to go for a stroll in the fields nearby.

Outside, fanned by the cool and fragrant breath of autumn, she felt immediately better. 'Let me see,' she said to herself, 'the palace is on the outskirts in the east. Where shall I go from here? To the north where I could get a glimpse of the woods from those cluster of monoliths, or to the south where I could climb the low hills for a panoramic view of the town?' Her lady-in-waiting, who had followed her, suggested it might be too late to go anywhere. Indeed, a light moon was already up in the eastern sky and a few stars were making their appearance at the edges of the horizon, but Lieng Makaw dismissed the woman and walked towards the knolls, instructing her to be around only when called for.

When she got to the nearest hill, the night was already bathed in the flaxen light of the moon and the surroundings were clear as day. The town was quiet and glimmering with flambeaux and hearth fires. She turned her gaze north-east to the cluster of monoliths—the male stones standing erect and the female ones lying flat at their feet, so that they looked to her like high-backed seats for the weary traveller. She felt strangely drawn to them and in spite of the advancing night, she found herself making her way towards them.

Lieng Makaw sat on a flat slab and leaned back against a standing male stone, sighing deeply as she brooded over her life, and a husband, who seemed to have lost all interest in her after barely a week of life together. And I'm bound to him for life, she thought bitterly. How will our life together be? Will I always be left to myself like this till the fire in my blood slowly dies for lack of caring hands?

As she sat there assailed by doubts and worrying over a thousand questions, the air abruptly came alive to the strains of the extraordinary music which she had heard the previous night. They rose as if from the depth of the earth and were picked up and carried forward by the light wind to be distributed among the lonely creatures of the night. Lieng Makaw pricked up her ears trying to place the direction of the melodies. They seemed to be emerging from a hut standing alone between the monoliths and the woods. She ran towards the hut like a pet animal, as if responding to the urgent calls of her master. Yes, the delightfully sweet, incredibly sad music was emerging from the hut. In her excitement, Lieng Makaw shouted, 'Hey *Bah*! Hey *Kong*![7] Who is in the house? May I come in?'

In response, the music stopped and there was only silence, even after Lieng Makaw had repeated her call several times. Uncertain and a little nervous, she retraced her steps and ran back towards the palace.

At the palace, she called her attendant and casually enquired about the solitary hut she had seen near the woods.

'That, Mahadei, is the hut of Manik Raitong. Yes, Mahadei, he is the one who goes about in sackcloth and ashes. He even smears his face with soot. Nobody knows exactly why, but everyone thinks it is because he has suffered so much in his young life. Yes, he lives completely alone. All his relations have died. He is the most miserable creature on earth.'

'Hmm,' thought Lieng Makaw, 'so that is the hut of Manik the Wretched. In that case it must have been him playing those haunting tunes. But if he is what they all say he is, how could he have been the one to play such music? And why does his music affect me so profoundly? It is as though it knows me intimately; as though it is my long-lost friend; and that deep inside me, I also know it and that is why I react to it with such spontaneous joy.' She rubbed her chin...could he be the one she recalled? No, how could he be? The other was so good-looking...and yet, could it be possible? It had been so long ago...

There was no sleep for Lieng Makaw that night. She was grappling with a different kind of restlessness, no longer the misery eating at her heart, but an excitement induced by the music and provocative thoughts about Manik Raitong. She twisted and turned in her bed, and then, at about midnight, she suddenly sat bolt upright. Yes, she could hear faint snatches of the melody beckoning to her like the barely audible voice of a friend calling from far away. The palace was asleep. She neatened herself and crept out into the moonlight. She ran all the way to the hut and then stopped at a distance to listen.

The music was full and round, as if it gushed from some hidden spring and emerged surging into the air, riding the waves like a silver thread. It soared above the trees, now high, now low, like a gliding eagle: it was the wind whispering dolefully among the trees; it was the rain pattering softly among the dead leaves of the forest; it was a brook gurgling eerily among the bushes; it was the rolling wail of a cicada; it was the forlorn sadness, the distressed call of *jyllob*[8] in the deep woods; it was the cry of a soul in despair, a soul whose agonies had translated into this sweet, unceasing lament.

The music seemed to be all of these to Lieng Makaw, as she took in the different tunes throbbing in the air. She was moved as never before by this melodious outpouring of grief. Each tune carried the haunting note of sorrow and each note was a sweet and painful thrust in her heart. It reeled her in as if at the end of a hooked line, into the mysterious world of the musician. She ran lightly onto the porch. She peeped into the hut. 'What! This is no Manik Raitong in sackcloth and ashes!' she exclaimed in a whisper.

Indeed what she was seeing was a man in the finery and the ceremonial robes of a king. The man was sitting on a wooden stool facing the hearth. The enthralling music that had possessed her was flowing from the man's breath through the seven openings of a thin bamboo tube—the seven mouths of the soul, the seven outlets of sorrow, the seven wonders of a music created by the very breath of life. It was by playing his fingers over the openings that he was creating the most hauntingly poignant tunes that Lieng Makaw had ever heard. Every time the man exhaled into the tube, a string tautened in her heart and tugged at her painfully.

She knocked loudly on the door. 'This is your mahadei, Ka Lieng Makaw, please open the door,' she requested.

The door did not open, but this time, the music did not stop either. Lieng Makaw peeped through the chink in the plank wall again, and without taking her eyes off his back, beat the timber frame with the palm of her hands, pleading, 'Please open the door, I only want to listen to your music. Please let me in, I only want to watch you playing.'

The man turned his face towards her. It was the handsome youth from the shyngiar! The youth who had loved her and sought her hand many years before! He was older, much more matured; otherwise he was the same, serene and attractive as ever. Yes, Manik was the man who was her first love! With her heart hammering in her side, she banged the wall more fiercely and shouted, 'Manik, it is I, the woman at the shyngiar! My name is Lieng Makaw, don't you remember me? You even came to my house to meet me...'

Manik was startled, she could see that, but then he simply turned away and began playing a different tune. As she listened spellbound to the new eerie tune, she seemed to understand everything. She was the last straw in his cheerless life, the last straw that broke his back. It was she who had turned him into the despised creature that he was now. She understood this as plainly as though he had recounted his story in clear and resounding terms. She became even more desperate. Manik's sharati gushed forth to draw out her very soul, which swirled about the porch like a mad spirit trying to find a way in. Lieng Makaw spotted a large machete leaning against the wall. She grabbed the broad, heavy knife and began battering the door with it till it finally broke down.

Lieng Makaw entered. Manik had stopped playing. He was standing and staring at her in amazement.

Lieng Makaw looked up at him with sheer adoration in her face. How she had secretly admired this fair, finely etched face, manly and majestic in its light yellow turban of muga silk. How fascinated she had been with these striking dark eyes shining with such a sad gentle light. She said, 'Don't you remember me? We met at the shyngiar years ago, you said you were in love with me; you...'

'I used to love a woman, not a queen,' Manik interrupted sadly. 'If you had shown your rebellious spirit then, we would have been happy. But now you have only sentenced me to death.'

It was a portentous statement from a man who had gained much wisdom from much suffering. But Lieng Makaw did not even stop to think. 'What wrong have I done?' she replied. 'I have only come to listen to your mournful and mesmerizing music, which has not allowed me to sleep or to rest even for a moment since I had first heard it. And no wonder it is so. Now I understand. For your sorrow is my sorrow.

'But I have done nothing wrong by coming here. We

have done nothing wrong...and besides, it is about midnight. Nobody knows and nobody needs to know.'

From that time Lieng Makaw started visiting Manik every night to hear him play; to listen to his magical sharati; to wonder how on earth he could have conjured up such enchanting notes.

Nobody knew that Manik Raitong, Manik the Wretched, Manik the Forsaken, had won the heart of a queen.

Time flew, the seasons passed and passed again over the land. But the syiem did not return. It was only at the end of the third winter that he sent word of his homecoming. The entire hima got ready to give its great and noble king a reception befitting a conquering hero. There was a great rejoicing in the land when the syiem reappeared. Every village received him with festivities and much show of affection. In the capital, however, the tone of welcome was muted. And in the palace, there was only a dreadful hush.

When the syiem arrived at the palace he first asked for his mahadei, 'Where is Ka Mahadei? Why isn't she here to receive me?'

A frightened household told him, 'She is suckling the baby, Pa'iem.'

'Baby! What baby!' thundered the startled syiem, jumping back as if he had stepped upon a snake.

The servants replied, 'Ka Mahadei's, Pa'iem.'

'What? Ka Mahadei has a baby? How is that? Why was no message sent to me?' he bellowed.

At that moment the queen mother appeared. 'Welcome home, son,' she said quietly. 'Come, we shall talk in private.'

When they were huddled alone in the main chamber, the queen mother asked, 'How long have you been absent?'

'Three winters, of course,' the syiem said impatiently.

'Then the baby is definitely not yours,' the queen mother concluded. 'We have always known this, of course, that's why we have put her under house arrest. I just want to make sure. The child is male. He is about six full moons old. The question is what is to be done now?'

The syiem clenched his fists, ground his teeth and hissed out with suppressed rage, 'I'm going to destroy the man who has brought this shame upon me, upon my house, upon the entire hima. And I'm going to destroy them both.'

'My feelings, exactly,' agreed the queen mother. 'But first you should find out from her who the man is. Not that she would tell you, knowing what you would do. But you could try.'

Lieng Makaw was summoned before the syiem. As the queen mother had deduced, it was useless to expect a disclosure from her. Here was no repentant woman. She came before the syiem with her head held high—proud, stubborn, unashamed and even happy. Seeing this, the syiem thought, 'Is she naively expecting me to merely throw her out, divorce her, so that she can live blissfully on with her paramour? Or does she think that her father, the Lyngskor, will protect her?' A hard cruel smile curved the left corner of his mouth as he dismissed her.

But what was to be done? He could not possibly have her physically forced into a confession, for after all, she was his legally wedded wife and the daughter of the hima's chief minister to boot. Later, he could devise an appropriate punishment for her, but for now, that method was out of the question. But what was then to be done?

It was the Lyngdoh Hima who suggested that a test be carried out to uncover the identity of the wrongdoer. On his instruction, he said, the shamans had already performed an egg divination ceremony, and God, U Nongap Jutang, the Keeper of the Covenant, the Pledge between Man and Him, had indicated, through signs, a way by which the syiem and the hima could expose the offender and right all wrongs.

To implement the test, a dorbar hima, comprising all those villages within striking distance from the capital, was convened. All marriageable male members from the villages were ordered to attend without fail and to bring with them a banana apiece.

On the appointed day, the men were made to form a circle around a huge field. At the head of the circle sat the syiem, the Lyngskor, the Lyngdoh Hima and other ministers. To their right and left, extending for thousands of paces, sat the councillors from the villages. The middle of the circle was left bare except for a cane mat on which lay Lieng Makaw's six-full-moon-old baby. The purpose of the dorbar was explained at length by the Lyngdoh Hima, following an instruction from the syiem. Each man was required to hold up the banana he had brought and to offer it to the baby. The man whose banana the baby accepted would be declared as its father and would be punished as deemed fit by the whole dorbar.

The procedure was initially objected to by many, for they pointed out the possibility of the baby accepting more than one banana, or accepting it from the wrong man. But the Lyngdoh Hima argued that the test was according to the signs and tokens indicated by God, and eventually persuaded everyone by contending that justice would be carried out only after a further careful investigation. The man whose banana was accepted by the baby, he said, would be subjected to additional examinations and questioning so that the absolute truth was first established.

After these assurances, the dorbar unanimously agreed to put the test into operation. The men, starting from the direction to the right of the syiem, carried the bananas in their hands, and with their hearts in their mouths, approached the baby.

The first one, a scrawny middle-aged man, gripped his banana in the fingers of his right hand, held it upright, and then crouching low, hand extended in a gesture of offering, he slowly crept towards the baby in the fashion of a man who was trying to appease an angry and dangerous animal. With sweat dripping from his forehead, he reached the baby and presented the banana, cooing softly and grinning foolishly. The whole dorbar held its breath. The baby looked at the man and then at the banana, but continued to suck its fingers. The man stood up, gave a loud sigh of relief, raised his hands and shook them in the air in jubilation.

And so, one by one, to the last man, each was subjected to the test—the younger men sweating under the strain, while the elderly were more perfunctory. One of them, a joker in the pack, even tried to thrust the banana into the baby's hands so he could be suspected of having made love to the queen. The baby, however, showed no interest in any of the bananas. Frustrated, the syiem nodded an instruction to the Lyngskor, who stood up and asked, 'Is there anyone from any of the villages who hasn't attended? Respected headmen, please answer for your groups.'

Each headman stood up and testified that every marriageable male member from his village had attended. But one headman from a locality of the capital stood up to explain, 'Everyone has attended, Pa'iem, except Manik Raitong. As you know, he lives like an outcast and goes about in sackcloth and ashes. His face is always covered with soot and grime. He is truly a wretched creature. Should such a man be called to the dorbar?'

At first the dorbar was divided in its opinion until the Lyngdoh Hima intervened. He said, 'I have just consulted with the other priests, Pa'iem, and they are unanimous that every male, regardless of his circumstances in life, must be called before the dorbar. I move, therefore, that Manik Raitong be brought here.'

Manik was brought to the dorbar and handed a banana. Timid and shy, he cut such a pathetic figure in his ragged and

ash-covered sackcloth that everyone present clucked in
sympathy and annoyance that such a one should be subjected
to such a test. The question on everybody's mind was how
the mahadei could possibly be expected to consort with such
a poor thing? '*Shish!*' they uttered in derision, 'he looks like
one of those beggars from the plains'.

Manik walked towards the baby with his banana. He was
no longer timid and shy. Erect as a tall stone, he advanced.
When he reached the baby he kneeled down and offered him
the banana. As soon as he saw Manik, the baby kicked out
his little hands and feet in excitement. He giggled and
gurgled and reached out towards Manik, wanting to be picked
up. Manik reached for him, hoisted him in the air and
announced imperiously, 'This is my son!'

A deafening roar went up throughout the dorbar. The
men jumped to their feet in amazement. They craned their
necks for a better look at Manik and exclaimed in sheer
disbelief that such a stinking wretch could have cuckolded
their syiem.

The syiem called for order. He could not believe that he
had been undone by this filthy half-human. He instructed the
Lyngskor to question Manik closely. He sent one of the
ministers to get Manik's claim confirmed by Lieng Makaw.
When everything was done and the truth was established
beyond the shadow of a doubt, the dorbar sentenced Manik
to immediate death by *u tangon u lymban*, that is, by crushing
his neck between two heavy logs.

Manik, unafraid and unperturbed, requested the dorbar
that a last wish be granted him. He began:

'You, the syiem, the mother; you the ministers, the
advisers; you the priests, the nobles; and you the councillors,
true sons of your mothers, in whom true power is vested;
please hear me out. You consider me a criminal to be
condemned to death by u tangon u lymban. But in my heart
of hearts, for reasons that you will come to know by and by,

I know that I am not a criminal. It is life's designs that I should suffer and through suffering create and conquer, and then suffer again for my very achievements. I'm not a lawbreaker the way a thief or a murderer is. My heart is pure, pure as a mountain stream. If someone is attracted to that purity and tries to drink from it that does not render the stream impure. I'm not, however, trying to justify my actions, nor am I trying to plead for clemency. Death is the natural end of all sorrows. All I ask is that I do not be slain like a common criminal. Please allow me to choose the manner of my own death.'

The dorbar was surprised by Manik's fluent self-expression. Even their renowned ruler had never attained such solemn eloquence. Amidst the hushed silence the syiem enquired, 'How would you like to meet your death?'

Without any hesitation Manik said, 'I would like to die by the cleansing power of fire. What I have done is unclean to you. What life has done is unclean to me. Let fire destroy every trace of my life, let my soul rise like the blue smoke and be one with the blue sky. And let me build my own pyre so that I may go in peace, having died by my own hand.'

The dorbar, moved to pity despite what it considered an unpardonable crime against the head of state, granted his unusual request. Even the hard-hearted among them said to themselves, 'Since he is going to die anyway, it does not matter to us how he meets his end.' A day was appointed and builders assigned to assist Manik in making the pyre. Guards were also posted to monitor Manik's movements.

Manik went about building the pyre as though he was making preparations for the most important occasion of his life. He selected a site on a small hill on the western edge of the town and had a large rectangular strip cleared. Then he ordered several huge plantain trunks, which he made into a spacious rectangular enclosure, open at the bottom and the top. The enclosure was fixed into the ground with fist-sized wooden spikes in such a way that the bottom rested on the wooden, latticed platform of a makeshift hearth. He packed a considerable stash of dry logs inside the enclosure and proceeded to decorate the pyre.

The plantain trunks were first covered with pure white cotton sheets and then beautified with dark red velvet, festooned with golden tassels. The corners of the decorated enclosure were topped by wooden carvings resembling a plantain flower called *siarkait*. Finally, four long bamboo poles were erected near the four corners of the pyre to which were attached the *shanduwa*, or a high canopy of deep red satin cloth.

When all this was done, Manik stood back to survey the place of his last repose. Satisfied with his own handiwork, he went home to prepare for his final journey.

On the day fixed for Manik's self-immolation, people streamed into the capital from all corners. They started arriving at first cockcrow and continued to flow in till the sun stood at the zenith. It was shortly after they had all settled down and chosen their vantage points near the funeral pyre that they heard the strains of eerie music floating towards them. They had never heard anything like these tunes before—onwards they came towards the pyre, like creeping tendrils in the air. Were they the spirits of the air, the harbingers of death, enticing the soul with sweet refrains? The music grew stronger, fuller, more doleful. It was now wheeling like a hawk, up and down, high and low, swirling about them, conveying anguish, heart-rending grief and deep lamentation.

Many among those present asked, 'What is that? Is it the wind whispering sadly among the trees? Is it the rain pattering softly among the dead leaves? Is it a brook gurgling eerily among the bushes? Is it the rolling wail of a cicada? Is it the forlorn sadness, the distressed call of a bird in the deep woods?'

However, they soon saw it was Manik Raitong, playing on his sharati, the very same instrument the local populace had dismissed as that of a mad man, but which was now haunting them with the forlorn, gently stabbing yet deeply wounding melodies Manik had fashioned from the repertoire of his singular sorrow. And how he looked! He was clean, and bathed, and handsome beyond belief. Tall and sinewy, he strode forward gaily, his head slightly tilted to the right, his lips kissing the mouth of the sharati and both his hands fondly fingering the rest of its slim body.

He was dressed like a royal dancer. He had donned a luxuriant dhoti of deep purple eri silk with silver edging over which he wore a white shirt and a sleeveless jacket adorned with ornate designs and the golden tassels of muga. Over this was draped an X-shaped chain of silver inlaid with ruby. On his neck was a pearl-shaped necklace of gold and red coral stones and on his head was a magnificent purple and gold mulberry silk turban topped with eagle feathers.

Watching the new Manik, the people were wonderstruck. They shouted among themselves, 'Is this Manik the Wretched, or Manik the Prince? Look at him clothed in the ceremonial robes of a king!' cried one of them.

'Yes!' cried another, 'in the finery of a spring dancer!'

Yet another asked, 'How is it we never knew that we have the prince of princes in our midst? Not only is he a well-endowed youth, but an accomplished musician as well! Why did we ever treat such a gem like a pariah?'

It seemed as if Manik had come to life in all his splendour just before the hour of his death. It seemed as if he had been discovered in all his enthralling powers just when he was about to be damned forever. Many people thought that it was neither just nor honourable to destroy such a God-gifted talent. They went to the syiem to plead on Manik's behalf, to spare his life and change his death sentence to life in exile. But the syiem sat there, flanked by his ministers, near the pyre, hard-faced and unmoved as a rock. He was watching Manik's curious behaviour.

Having reached the top of the hill, Manik turned his back to the pyre and walked backwards towards it—he was withdrawing from life, having a last look at it, while his sharati was sending its last greetings to his queen. Now he was truly playing his heart out, piping the most poignant and affecting dirges of his life. The sweet-bitter tunes, tinged with black despair, were like barbed arrows going straight for the hearts of the onlookers and drawing tears of pain from their regretful eyes.

When he arrived at the pyre, Manik set the dry logs on fire then turned to circle the blazing flames three times. At the same time as he began his slow circular motion, he abruptly changed the tune of his music. The sharati was no longer mourning his dismal fate. It became festive and triumphant, shaping a new image of Manik, the consummate artiste who, having won the love of a queen through an art that was also winning the hearts of all those who had initially come to enjoy the spectacle of his fiery end, was now happy to make a sacrifice of his life.

After he had circled the pyre three times, Manik stopped by the crackling blaze. He passed the sharati through the fire three times and then threw it across the pyre another three times. Having done this he went to a corner and planted it upside down on the ground—a powerful and profound gesture, both an indication and a denouncement of how the society had treated him and his art. Then, without further ado, he jumped into the roaring inferno.

All this time Lieng Makaw was confined to her room at the palace, and her guards had strict instructions not to let her out of their sight. But the spectacular metamorphosis of Manik dressed in royal robes and playing what seemed to them a transformed and mesmerizing sharati, had caused such a frenzied tumult that everyone deserted his post to have a glimpse at this spectacle of a lifetime.

Lieng Makaw heard the familiar lingering notes of sweet sadness and her soul immediately broke into a dust devil dance. She moved about the room like a restless spirit, and without knowing why, she found herself putting on her best clothes. When the music stopped as Manik passed out of earshot, she also stopped, wondering fearfully what had happened to him. She was suddenly assailed by an empty feeling as though everything had been scraped out from inside her, leaving her with nothing but a hollow shell. She wailed out in despair, 'What use is this cage without its *maina*?'[8] And so she rushed out, flying like the wind, towards the cremation hill.

When she arrived there, almost unnoticed by anyone, she was in time to see Manik throwing himself into the fire. She gave one shrill agonizing cry, 'Maniiik!' And then, before anyone could stop her, she was already in the burning pyre with the only love of her life.

A deep gloom fell upon the gathering. They had never witnessed such an event in their lives. They had never known such extraordinary souls before. They dispersed slowly, with a bitter taste in their mouths and an unclean feeling in their hearts.

The next morning, when the Lyngdoh Hima, along with the other priests and some elders went to perform the purgatorial rites at the site, they found to their amazement that a spring was gushing forth from the spot where the funeral pyre had been. And where the sharati had been planted upside down was a cluster of thin bamboos with leaves slanting downwards. Near the bamboo cluster was the sprout of a new tree species with large boat-shaped leaves that was later to be called the Lieng Makaw tree.

Though the names of the great syiem and his expansive hima have become shrouded in the mists of time, perhaps deliberately, the thin-stem bamboos with inverted leaves could be found till the latter part of the twentieth century on the hill that has come to be known as U Lum Raitong. The spring still exists and now serves the requirements of Raitong, a new village that had sprung up near the hill many years after the destruction of the original capital town by unknown invaders. The Lieng Makaw tree still grows in plenty in the area and they say that if there was a truly inspired sharati player nearby, its leaves would dance, even when there was no breeze in the air.

And the melancholy sharati survives in spite of Manik burying it upside down. It has now become the most favoured instrument played during any sad occasion, but especially as an instrument of lament during cremation ceremonies. Its shorter version, the *besli*, or flute, on the other hand, has transformed itself into a quintessential instrument of love, used in traditional Khasi courtships.

---

[1]The names of both the capital and the hima are unknown, perhaps deliberately kept a secret to protect the identity of the syiem.

[2]Khasi outer garment comprising two long cloths of cotton, silk, etc., draped over the shoulders.

[3] The matrilineal Khasis do not accord the title of Ka Syiem or Queen to the wife of U Syiem, the King. The wife of U Syiem is called Ka Mahadei, although she is sometimes unofficially addressed as queen. The proper title of Ka Syiem is held by the syiem's mother or his eldest sister.

[4]The Himalayas.

[5] The King Junior.

[6]A term of respect and endearment for the Syiem.

[7]Respectful terms of address: Bah for Mr and Kong for Miss or Sister.

[8]Songbird of the lorikeet family.

Acknowledgements

Most of the stories in this book would not have been written if it had not been for the compulsion of the Sunday Supplement of *Apphira Daily News*, an English-language newspaper that I edited between 1994 and 1996. The need to fill in the supplement with something literary, cultural and unique, and the want of contributors on such subjects, led to my exploration of Khasi myths, the accurate retelling of which was another long-felt need. The twenty folk stories in this book were collected for the supplement during 1994 and 1995. My gratitude is, therefore, owed firstly to the aesthetic interest of the paper's management.

The vague thought of putting the stories together in a book someday, became a real ambition when I first met Sally Roberts Jones of Alun Books in Port Talbot during the Khasi writers' tour of Wales in 1995. Nigel Jenkins, our manager during the tour, introduced me to Sally, who showed a keen interest in the stories. Sally has promised to give them an identity of their own through her Alun Books. *Khublei shibun* Sally, *diolch yn fawr* to you and Nigel.

But it is to Penguin that I owe the greatest gratitude for being the first to publish the stories, and thereby, according the Khasi community a place in the sun. To Prita, especially, for being such an attentive editor and my first true critic.

My close friend Pankaj Thapa has helped in bringing the stories to life with his very apt sketches. My sincere thanks, Panks!

My gratitude is also due to the following journals and anthologies where some of the stories had appeared in English and Hindi:

Indian Literature (Sahitya Akademi, New Delhi), *New Frontiers* (North-East Writers' Forum, Guwahati), *Fresh Fictions* (Katha, New Delhi), *First Sun Stories* (Katha, New Delhi), *U Sier Lapalang* (Katha, New Delhi), *INSA Newsletter* (Indian Society of Authors, New Delhi), *Aam Admi* (All India Tribal Literary Forum, New Delhi), *IIC Quarterly* (India International Centre, New Delhi), *Lasubon 2005* (East Zone Inter-University Youth Festival Souvenir, Shillong) and *The Shillong Times* (Shillong).

I dedicate this book to my mother and my departed uncle, who told me the first stories.